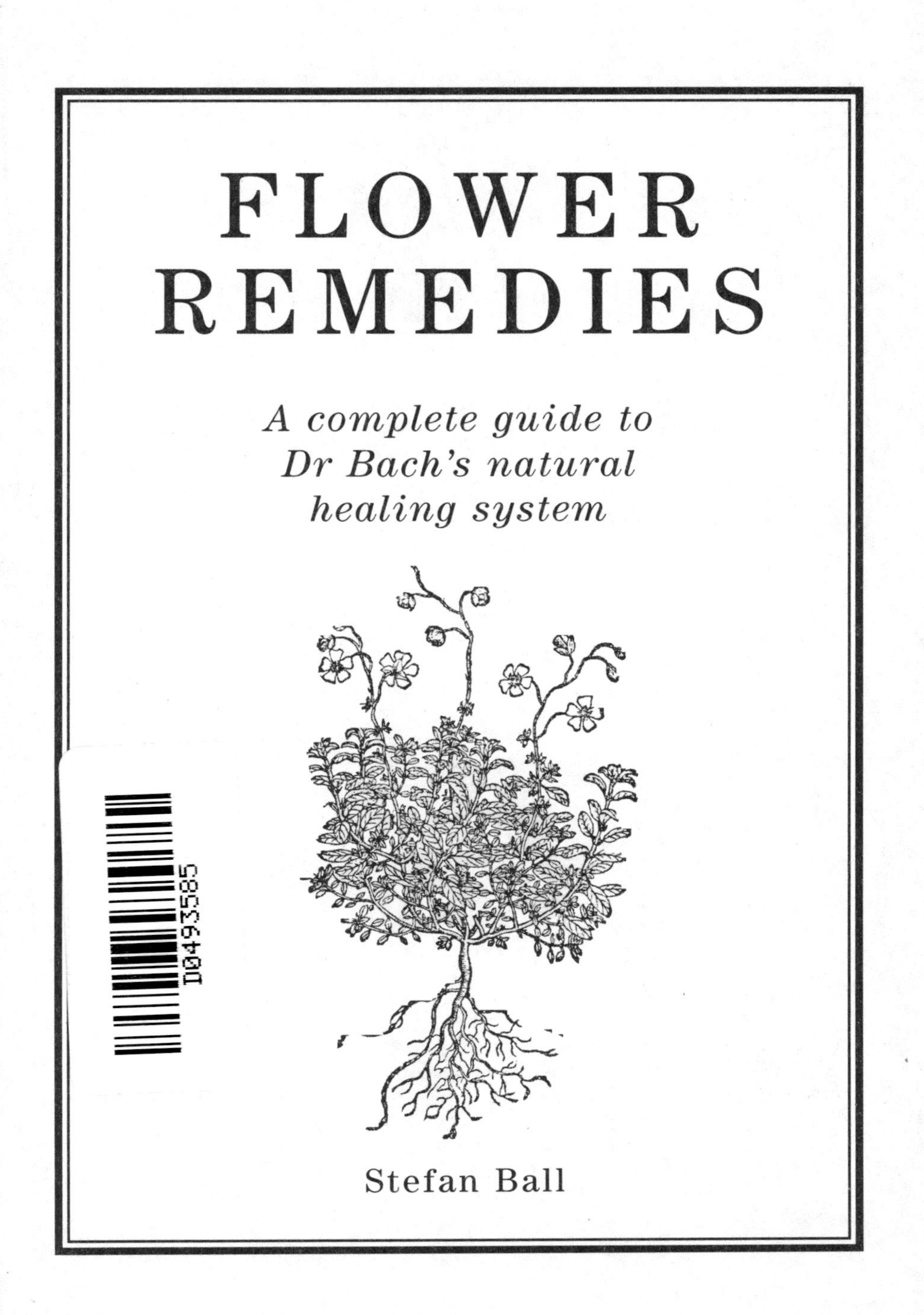
FLOWER
REMEDIES
A complete guide to
Dr Bach's natural
healing system
Stefan Ball

Published by Blitz Editions
an imprint of Bookmart Ltd
Registered Number 2372865
Trading as Bookmart Ltd
Desford Road
Enderby
Leicester LE9 5AD

This book created by Amazon Publishing Ltd, Middlesex
Editor: Diana Russell
Assistant editor: Jasmine Brown
Design: Wilson Design Associates
Cover photography: Andrew Kolesnikow
Printed and bound in Great Britain

ISBN 1-85605-329-6

SAFETY NOTE

Throughout the book *asterisks refer to important safety information placed in boxes below the marked text. Please read these notes carefully.

AUTHOR'S NOTE

All recommendations contained in this book are believed by the author to be effective if properly administered and if the correct remedies are used. However, the author has no control over the remedies used by others or the manner in which they are used, and the author cannot guarantee the effectiveness of their use or be held in any way liable.

If you are in any doubt about the nature of your illness, the author strongly recommends you seek the advice of your doctor or other qualified medical practitioner.

CONTENTS

INTRODUCTION

This book is a practical introduction to healing yourself and others with flower remedies. Everything you need is here, including information on preparing and taking the remedies, full details of the various mental and emotional states they can be used to treat, and numerous examples of the remedies in action.

In addition, there are chapters specifically aimed at women, men and children respectively, each dealing with problems peculiar to those groups and giving details of how the remedies might be used to help.

Although the remedies are safe, there are some precautionary and other considerations you should be aware of, particularly if you want to prepare the remedies yourself from trees and flowers growing wild. Throughout the book, safety information and other important notes are presented in boxes and marked with an *asterisk. Please take time to read these parts carefully.

If you prefer to buy the remedies ready-prepared and are unable to find them in your local chemists, the Bach Centre can help you to find a local stockist, or else you can buy them by mail order from a homoeopathic pharmacy. Addresses are given at the end of the book. Should you want further advice or to consult a trained flower remedy practitioner, the Bach Centre can give you information to help you find exactly what you need.

Flower remedies can be used by anyone. I hope that this book will encourage you to take your first steps towards using them, so that you can join the many other people throughout the world who have benefited from this simple and effective therapy.

The author would like to express his gratitude to everyone at the Bach Centre in Oxfordshire for their kindness and help with the preparation of this book. Some of the case histories have been taken from the Bach Centre's records, but in all cases names and other details have been changed to preserve the anonymity of the people treated.

Special thanks go to Judy Howard at the Centre, who read through the whole book in manuscript and suggested numerous improvements and corrections. Any faults that remain despite her vigilance are of course the fault of the author alone.

Something more than gratitude is due to my wife Chris and daughters Alex and Maddie, but they know that already.

CHAPTER 1

Dr Bach's Discoveries

It is a commonplace nowadays to say that such things as stress, trauma, worry, anger and insecurity can cause physical illness. Everyone knows that if you are unhappy you are more likely to fall ill. Perhaps this is why the flower remedies discussed in this book, which act on spiritual and emotional states, have become so popular and so widely respected in the last twenty or so years. In fact the idea of curing physical complaints by addressing emotional causes is so accepted now that it can take an effort of imagination to think back to a time when this was not the case.

The discovery of the remedies, their preparation and their method of use were all the work of one man: Dr Edward Bach. Bach trained at University College Hospital, London, in the days when doctors were used to looking at the physical symptoms they were faced with, and looking at them in isolation, ignoring the whole person in order to focus their physical interventions on a part only. But Bach was an original thinker even in his student days, and it soon became apparent to him that although several people might have the same disease, in many cases different treatments were needed to cure them. Furthermore, the same treatments could be used in different cases to treat different diseases. He saw the need to look at the whole patient, including the personality, in order to arrive at a sound diagnosis and find a suitable therapy.

Bach qualified as a doctor in 1912. His first job was at University College Hospital (UCH), where he was Casualty Medical Officer. He then became Casualty House Surgeon at the National Temperance Hospital, London. After a few months he resigned the post due to ill health and instead opened his own consulting rooms in Harley Street. His interest in research led him to go back to UCH as a bacteriologist, working on vaccines against arthritis and other chronic illnesses.

When war broke out in 1914, Bach was turned down

by the army as too ill to serve. Nevertheless, and in addition to his private practice and his research work, he took on responsibility for 400 beds set aside for casualties, and in 1915 began additional bacteriological work at the UCH Medical School.

Given the poor state of his health, it was no surprise that all this overwork eventually took its toll. In July 1917 Bach suffered a haemorrhage which left him unconscious. He was operated on at once to remove a growth, but when he recovered consciousness was told that he only had about three months to live.

As soon as he was able to get out of bed, Bach returned to his laboratory work, believing that as he had only a short time left he must make one last effort to leave as little undone as possible. He worked every hour of the day and into the night, becoming so wrapped up in the excitement and effort of research that before he knew it the three months were past and yet, strangely, he was getting stronger and feeling fitter. As Nora Weeks later told the story in *The Medical Discoveries of Edward Bach, Physician*, so unexpected was this recovery that a friend who bumped into him at this time greeted him with the words: 'But, good God! Bach, you're dead!'

Bach took his own case as further evidence of the power of mental states over physical symptoms. He was convinced that his survival was due to his commitment to a purpose and his desire to get well – and that if he could find a way to release this energy in other people he would have a truly potent weapon against disease.

To further his research work Bach set up his own laboratory. It was partly to finance this that in 1919 he started work at the London Homoeopathic Hospital, where he was pathologist and bacteriologist.

This encounter with homoeopathy was decisive for Bach. Not only did it reinforce his view that every individual was different and so might need a different cure, it also gave him a clue to the direction his own work would follow, since for the most part homoeopathy was using

natural ingredients taken from plants rather than the neutralized bacteria that he himself had worked on up till then. And it was founded on the principle that less is more: in other words, the idea that the smallest possible amount of a remedy could be more effective and at the same time avoid all the unpleasant side effects often associated with more conventional medicine.

Bach started using homoeopathic procedures in his own research, with great success, and he continued research in this direction after he left the Homoeopathic Hospital in 1922. But he still felt that there was something amiss with the way he was going about things. This feeling came to a head in 1930 when he abruptly abandoned his Harley Street practice and its £5,000 a year income (a considerable sum in those days) in order to start the search for the simplest and most natural system of healing he could find. Instinctively he knew that nature would provide the ingredients he needed, and it was with this in mind that he left London.

Bach had noticed while researching a series of seven homoeopathic remedies (still in use, and known as 'the seven Bach nosodes') that although it was impossible to tell by looking at physical symptoms alone which nosode would work best, if you looked first at a patient's emotional state you could quickly see a pattern emerging. People who were prone to sudden attacks of anger responded to one type of remedy, while those who tended to be withdrawn and nervous needed another. Bach decided to make this theory of personality types the basis of his new healing system. His guiding principle became 'Treat the person, not the disease'.

From 1930 to 1934 Bach moved around the countryside, from Wales in the west to Norfolk in the east. The first remedies he found were based on common plants, all non-poisonous and almost without exception native wild flowers. He found that the potency of the flowers could be transferred to pure spring water through the action of the sun, and for this reason the years took on a natural pattern of their own: he sought out new plants in the summer months, when the sun was strong enough to prepare the remedies; while the winters were spent using the new remedies to treat patients and planning the next year's activity.

In 1934 Bach decided to end his nomadic existence and rented a little cottage in the village of Sotwell in Oxfordshire. With this as his base the pace of his work increased. To the nineteen remedies he had already found he added a further nineteen, some prepared by the sun method and some by boiling, which was necessary to deal with some of the tougher, woodier plants that he was now working with: walnut, larch and hornbeam, for example.

By the time Dr Bach died in 1936, some nineteen years after being told he had only three months to live, his work was complete. Taken in combination, the thirty-eight remedies he had found covered every conceivable mental and emotional state, and he had gathered a few faithful friends who had sworn to keep his work alive.

Today the flower remedies discovered by Dr Edward Bach are used by people all over the world. Their popularity continues to grow, and many doctors and other health professionals use them as a safe and beneficial complement to orthodox medicine. They have also been incorporated into several other forms of alternative medicine – for example aromatherapy, reflexology and iridology. But their main use is the one that Dr Bach himself wanted to see: people understanding and taking control of their own emotions and health with the help of remedies that they prescribe for themselves. For Bach's great aim and great achievement was simplicity in all things, and above all in the use of the remedies. 'I want to make it as simple as this,' he would say to Nora Weeks, who recorded his words. 'I am hungry, I will go and pull a lettuce from the garden for my tea; I am frightened and ill, I will take a dose of mimulus.'

CHAPTER 2

HOW THE REMEDIES ARE MADE

The flower remedies are all made from non-poisonous flowers and pure water. The methods used to make them are simple and natural, typifying the purity and simplicity of the remedies, so it is possible to make them for yourself.

Nevertheless, there are certain problems involved in preparing the remedies for yourself, and it is as well to be aware of these right from the outset. There are a number of poisonous plants growing wild in Britain which are toxic if ingested, and some of them are so poisonous that it can be extremely dangerous even to touch them. These include notorious killers such as deadly nightshade, bleeding heart, henbane and 'lords and ladies', as well as more common plants such as members of the buttercup family (*Ranunculaceae*) and the autumn crocus (*Colchicum autumnale*). As long as the correct plants and methods are used, all the flower remedies and the flowers used to make them are entirely safe, but it is important to be aware of the toxicity which does exist in the countryside and to appreciate how important it is to choose the correct plant.

There are many varieties of nearly all the remedy plants and this can make identification extremely difficult. This means that you need to be very selective and careful when gathering materials for a remedy. There are no substitutes for the plants whose Latin names appear in chapter 4: near misses will in all likelihood not do you any harm, but neither will they do you any good since the healing properties you want will not be released. Use a good guide to wild flowers, preferably one with really detailed, coloured illustrations, to help you find the exact plants you need. Also, check the descriptions in chapter 4 carefully, noting the size and shape of the leaves and the colour of the flowers, their position on the stem or twig and any other details you can. And again, if in doubt about the plant you want, do not pick it. It is of course illegal to uproot or pick any wild flower without the landowner's permission.

One mistake is to start the search for the remedy plants in your own back garden. This is not a good idea because (with one exception) only wild flowers are used for flower remedies. The plant growing where it chooses, in its natural habitat, is stronger and more wholesome and more easily transmits its healing properties to the water used to prepare it.

The one exception to this rule is the cerato (or *Ceratostigma willmottiana*), which is not native to Britain and can only be found growing in gardens.

Vine and olive are the other plants that are not found wild in Britain; if you want to prepare these remedies you will have to travel to the Mediterranean and make them there. Hothouse varieties grown in greenhouses will not do – and in any case the British sun is not hot enough for them to be prepared properly. And just as vine and olive plants grown in Britain should not be used, so varieties of British wild flowers that may be found in other parts of the world are also unsuitable. This is because the healing properties of each individual remedy are not dependent on species alone: climate, soil conditions and the time of year that the plant flowers are just as important.

You also need to be aware that, sadly, all too many wild flowers are disappearing from the countryside due to intensive farming, building and other demands on the land. It goes without saying that the whole philosophy of the remedies is based on a profound respect for nature and all its works, so if you do decide to try making your own remedies you should either only pick flowers that are very common – as is the case with, for example, white and red chestnut and the gorse – or choose sites where there are many flowers of the type you want growing together, so that after you have gone there will be plenty of flowering heads left to make sure of next year's bloom. Above all, never pick a flower if you do not know what it is, since it may be rare and perhaps protected by law.

In any case, whether you decide to make a remedy for yourself or you just want to enjoy the experience of seeing these often beautiful plants growing in their natural surroundings, there is a great deal of joy to be had in searching them out and in understanding where the flower remedies have their source.

METHODS OF PREPARATION

There are two methods used to prepare flower remedies, but they are not interchangeable. In other words, each remedy must be prepared using the method laid down for it. The following remedies are always made using the first of these, the ***sun method***:

agrimony, centaury, cerato, chicory, clematis, gentian, gorse, heather, impatiens, mimulus, oak, olive, rock rose, rock water, scleranthus, vervain, vine, water violet, white chestnut, wild oat.

The other method, known as the ***boiling method***, is used to prepare remedies that involve woody plants or the woody parts of plants, since these require more breaking down before they will release their potency. It is also used for those plants that bloom at times of the year when the sun is too weak to use the sun method with any success. The following remedies are prepared using this method:

aspen, beech, cherry plum, chestnut bud, crab apple, elm, holly, honeysuckle, hornbeam, larch, mustard, pine, red chestnut, star of Bethlehem, sweet chestnut, walnut, wild rose, willow.

The sun and boiling methods are fully described by Dr Bach in his 1936 book *The Twelve Healers and Other Remedies*. It details the sun method as follows:

> *A thin glass bowl is taken and almost filled with the purest water obtainable, if possible from a spring nearby.*
>
> *The blooms of the plant are picked and immediately floated on the surface of the water, so as to cover it, and then left in the bright sunshine for three or four hours, or less time if the blooms begin to show signs of fading. The blossoms are then carefully lifted out and the water poured into bottles so as to*

half fill them. The bottles are then filled up with brandy to preserve the remedy.

The boiling method is described like this:

The specimens were boiled for half an hour in clean pure water. The fluid strained off, poured into bottles until half filled, and then, when cold, brandy added as before to fill up and preserve. Chestnut Bud: For this remedy the buds are gathered from the White Chestnut tree, just before bursting into leaf.

In others the blossom should be used together with small pieces of stem or stalk and, when present, young fresh leaves.

Once the sun or boiling method has been used to produce a remedy as described above, the result is known as a 'mother tincture'. This is a highly concentrated form of the remedy and will keep its potency for many years – some of Dr Bach's original mother tinctures are still in storage at the Bach Centre, and they are as potent now as they ever were.

Before the remedies are ready to use they are diluted into a 'stock bottle'. This is done by filling a small dropper bottle with brandy, almost to the top, then adding two drops of the mother tincture to the bottle.

READY-PREPARED REMEDIES

The stock bottle is the same strength as the pre-prepared flower remedies that you can buy from most good health stores, chemists and pharmacies. All you have to do is dilute them into treatment bottles or just take the drops in water or fruit juice. (Full details on preparing treatment bottles and general information on how to take the remedies are given in chapter 3.)

The remedies available commercially are still made at Mount Vernon, the cottage in Oxfordshire where Dr Bach spent the last years of his life, and most of them are prepared from flowers gathered from sites he first discovered in the 1930s. The advantage of buying them ready-prepared is that you will know for certain that the correct plants and methods have been used, which means that you can rely on their purity and know that they will not harm you.

If you have trouble finding ready-prepared remedies locally, contact one of the organizations listed in the Appendix.

CHAPTER 3

TAKING THE REMEDIES

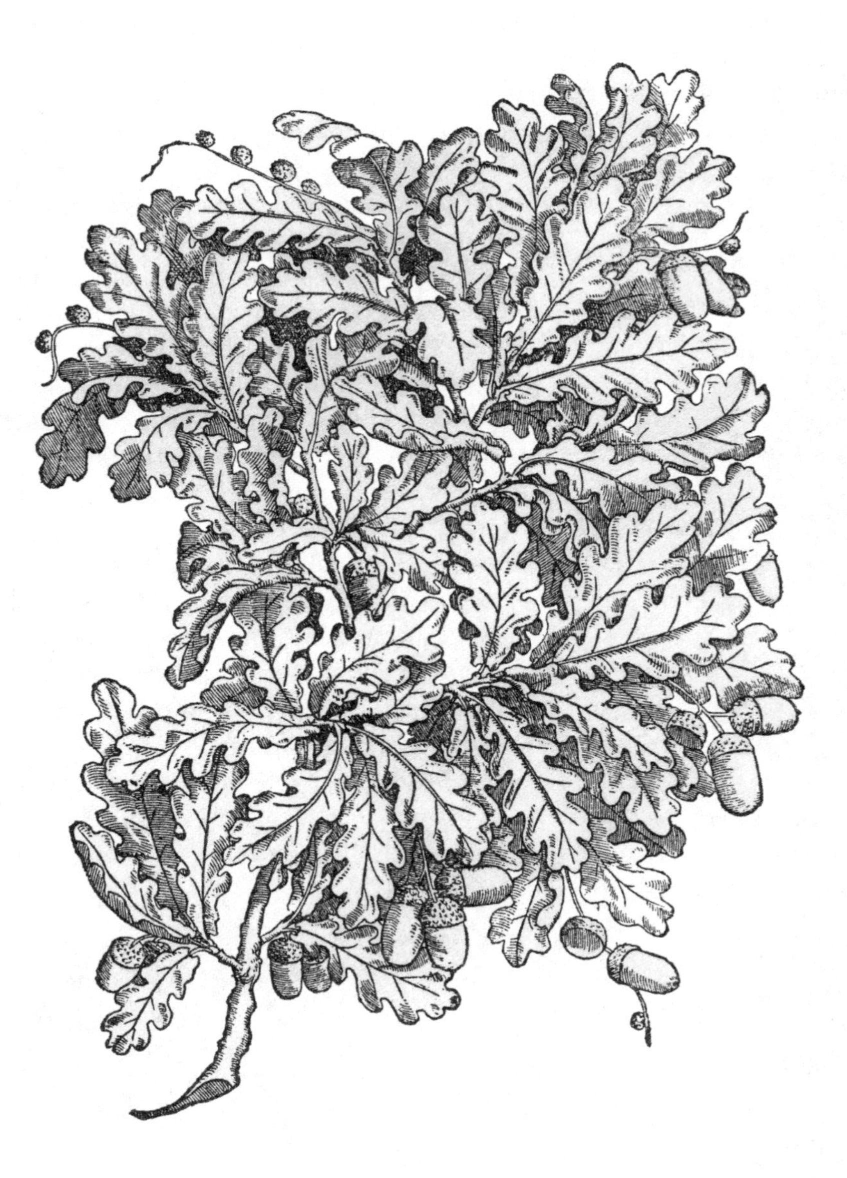

PREPARING TREATMENT BOTTLES

There are several ways to take the remedies. If you are treating a long-term condition – in other words, anything more than a temporary state – you will probably want to prepare a 'treatment bottle'. This is simply a 30 millilitre (1 fluid ounce) dropper bottle which contains the correct number of drops of the remedy or remedies you want, mixed with water and ready to take. You can buy the dropper bottles from any large chemist.

Treatment bottles are the most convenient and economical way to treat a long-term problem, since a single bottle can last up to three weeks. They are particularly useful when more than a single remedy is indicated.

Suppose for example that you are suffering from a chronic rash. You might decide that you are the impatiens type and that your irritation and impatience are causing the rash, but it makes you feel unclean – which calls for crab apple – and you can't stop worrying about it – which indicates the need for white chestnut. By making up a treatment bottle you can carry all three remedies around with you, ready-prepared in a single dropper bottle. The alternative is to take the separate stock bottles around with you, but (as you will see below) if you do this you will end up using a great deal more of the precious stock remedies, as well as suffering the added inconvenience of carrying around several bottles instead of one.

You do not need to make up a treatment bottle if you do not want to. Instead you can take drops of the stock remedy directly in a glass of water. See later on in this chapter for more information.

To prepare a treatment bottle, follow these steps:

1. Decide on the remedy or remedies that you think are required.
2. From the stock bottle(s) take two drops of each of the remedies you have chosen and put them into a 30 millilitre dropper bottle.

   If the dropper bottle is a new one you can use it straight away. If you are reusing a bottle that you have used before you will need to sterilize it first. To do this, place it in a saucepan, in pure, non-carbonated mineral water, and slowly bring it to the boil for twenty minutes. When the bottle has cooled, dry it thoroughly.
3. Top up the new treatment bottle with pure, uncarbonated spring or mineral water. Don't use carbonated water, as this has a tendency to fizz up over the sides.
4. Replace the cap firmly and label the bottle with the remedy or remedies it contains, the date and the word 'treatment'.

If you expect to be using the same treatment bottle for more than about ten days, it's a good idea to add a teaspoonful of brandy to the bottle before sealing it. This will help to preserve the remedy mixture and keep it fresh for longer. But even with the added brandy, the contents will not last for more than three weeks; any of the mixture left after this time should be discarded. In practice you will find that if you are taking the recommended dosage regularly enough the bottle will be empty before this anyway.

USING TREATMENT BOTTLES

Take four drops from the treatment bottle, on the tongue or in a glass of water, four times a day. The first dose should ideally be taken first thing in the morning, then take the others at approximately equal intervals, with the last dose taken just before going to bed.

The drops can be taken straight from the treatment bottle and dropped on the tongue using a pipette, or taken in a spoonful of water or fruit juice, or simply added to whatever drink you normally have: water, orange squash, tea, even beer or wine. Ideally you should think about the remedy as you take it, holding it in your mouth for a few moments before you swallow it, and visualizing the power of the remedy as it washes away negative thoughts and emotions.

In a sudden crisis you can increase the dosage as required, for example taking a full dose every ten, twenty or thirty minutes and then gradually increasing the gap between doses as your normal state of mind returns.

While taking more doses in a shorter space of time can help deal with a crisis, there is no point in taking stronger doses. Drinking a bottle of undiluted stock remedy instead of taking drops from a treatment bottle in the normal way will not be any more effective – although the brandy used to preserve the remedy will be. However, as you cannot overdose on the remedies themselves, there is no actual danger involved in taking more than the recommended dosage.

TAKING THE STOCK REMEDIES IN WATER

Although a treatment bottle is ideal for long-term conditions that are perhaps the result of a deep-rooted emotional state, it is impracticable for those unexpected and temporary states that we can all fall into. If you suffer from a sudden depression or feel a momentary sense of fear or indecision, there is little point in taking the time to make up a treatment bottle when what you want is some help now.

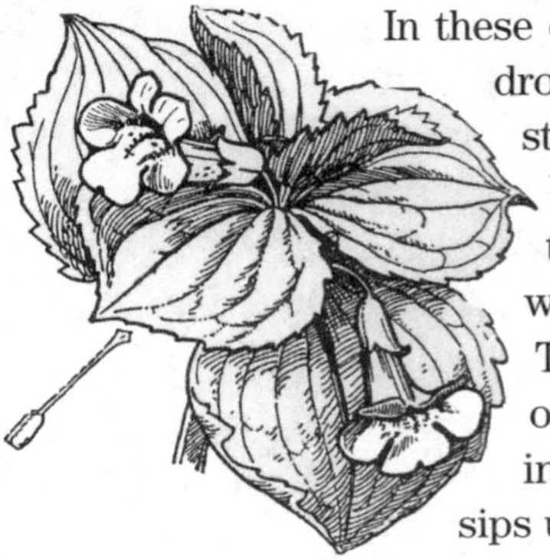

In these cases the most convenient method is to add drops of the indicated remedies directly from the stock bottles into a glass of water, or any other beverage. You can of course take long-term treatments in this way as well, although you will find it is cheaper to use a treatment bottle. The dosage is as follows. Into a glass of water or other beverage add two drops of the indicated stock remedies, and take frequent sips until the mood or other crisis has passed.

Never give remedies straight from the stock bottle to anyone who is a practising or recovering alcoholic. You should always warn anyone who you think might have a medical, moral or religious objection to alcohol that the remedies are preserved in brandy.

EMERGENCY TREATMENTS

There may sometimes be occasions when a remedy is needed but there are no glasses of water to hand, let alone time to make up a treatment bottle. In these cases the remedies can be dropped onto the tongue *direct from the stock bottles – but be warned that the *brandy used to preserve them will give any remedies taken in this way a rather strong taste.

EXTERNAL APPLICATIONS

The remedies can also be applied externally. Crab apple, the cleansing remedy, is often used in this way, for example to clean cuts and grazes or to help soothe skin disorders. Similarly, impatiens can be used where itches and other skin irritations seem to be linked to an emotional or mental irritation, or rock water can be applied where physical stiffness is caused by mental rigidity.

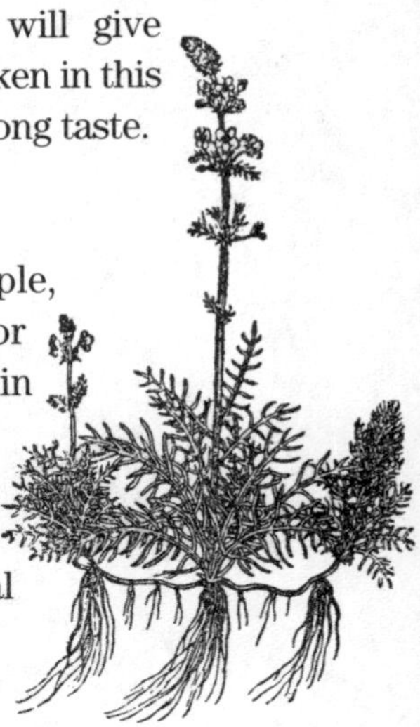

The simplest way to do this is to dilute the chosen remedies in a glass of water in the usual way and then gently bathe the affected area, or dab on the liquid using a fresh piece of cotton wool. For an all-over treatment, some people like to add the drops to a warm bath. In the case of the composite Rescue Remedy (see chapter 5), there is even a specially prepared cream which can be used for traumas such as *minor burns, cuts and grazes and so on.

Only very minor burns should be treated with the Rescue Remedy cream, or indeed any other type of cream. The best advice for any burn is to seek immediate medical attention if it is anything more than minor.
Remember that flower remedies are not designed to replace orthodox medical attention where there is physical injury or disease.

Another method is to use a cold compress. This is especially useful if there has been a sprain or swelling of any kind. Fill a small bowl with very cold water – you can add ice cubes as well if you want – and add two drops of each of the selected remedies. If you are using Rescue Remedy, add four drops. Dip a clean cloth in the mixture, just enough to wet it, and hold it against the affected area.

Using the same method with warm water, you can make a warm compress that can help ease stiffness.

In all this, however, it is important not to lose sight of the fact that the flower remedies treat mental and emotional conditions; they do not work directly on physical illness. There is no question, for example, of applying impatiens to every irritable rash you have. Instead, you need to

Call a doctor if the person you are treating is unconscious for more than a few seconds. If a child loses consciousness call a doctor immediately.
Motor and other travel accidents may result in internal injury. In such cases, call an ambulance at once and do not move anyone who is unable to move unaided.

locate the inner cause of the rash and treat the state of mind rather than the symptom. The only partial exception to this is crab apple, which can be taken orally, in the usual way, in any case where a cleansing is called for, including a physical cleansing.

External applications are in general an addition to the main treatment and are given in order to help things along a little – they are not a replacement for that treatment. The only exception to this rule is where the person being treated is unable to take the remedies in the normal way, perhaps because he or she is *unconscious or unable to swallow. In such cases remedies can be rubbed on the person's lips or gums, behind the ears, or on the wrists or temples. Star of Bethlehem, for example, might be given in this way if a person is in deep shock following an accident. For more on treating this kind of case see chapter 5, which deals with the composite Rescue Remedy.

FLOWER REMEDIES AND OTHER TREATMENTS

Although they are often thought of as alternative medicines, it would be more correct to think of the flower remedies as complementary medicines. They work well with all other forms of treatment, whether mainstream Western medicine or therapies such as aromatherapy, herbalism, yoga, osteopathy, acupuncture or homoeopathy. In all cases there is no conflict between the action of the flower remedies and the drugs and techniques used by these other traditions.

> *The remedies are safe to take at all times of life, including pregnancy. If you are pregnant, however, it is always best to tell the doctor or other health professional who is looking after you all about any medicine that you want to take.*

Having said this, some practitioners of other forms of therapy might advise you not to take any other medicines while following a course of treatment that they have prescribed for you. Homoeopaths in particular sometimes insist that no other medicines or drugs should be used. Although none of the flower remedies described in this book interfere in any way with homoeopathic or any other remedies, it is only fair to the person treating you to keep him or her informed of any other treatments that you might be following, including flower remedies.

Unfortunately, sometimes people go too far in combining the remedies with other treatments, to such an extent that they forget that flower remedies treat emotional states, and begin to use them as if they are aimed at particular diseases or symptoms. It cannot be stressed enough that the whole basis of the remedies' action is that *they only work on the body by way of the emotions and moods*, and it is these emotions and moods that need to be looked at when prescribing remedies.

Along the same lines, enthusiasts for other forms of treatment or for particular spiritual or occult techniques have at times abandoned the straightforward methods of prescribing and of taking the remedies that is set out here. Again it must be stressed that the flower remedies are a complete treatment in their own right.

There really is no substitute for the direct examination of moods and feelings, and this is the only way to arrive at a satisfactory diagnosis.

For full information on how to prescribe for yourself and for other people, see chapters 6 and 7.

In brief then, the message is this: the remedies can be used with any other medicine, but should only be prescribed following a real attempt to understand the negative emotions and thoughts that might be causing a particular problem. If it is felt that astrology, tarot cards, dowsing or any other technique might be of use in aiding this process, that is for each individual to decide – but such techniques should only ever be used as an addition to the normal exploration of the person's emotional state. They should never be allowed to take its place.

WHEN TO STOP TAKING THE REMEDIES

Unlike some modern drugs which are so powerful (and dangerous) that you have to take a predetermined number of pills or capsules in order to wean yourself off them, the flower remedies are very gentle and subtle in their action and can be discontinued at any time. Quite simply, you can stop taking them as soon as you feel better.

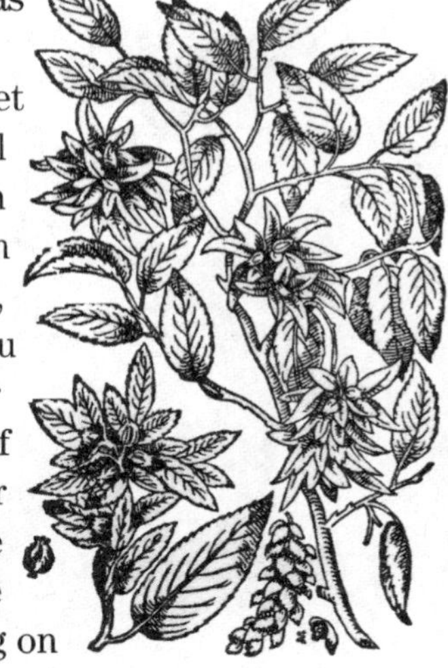

But how long should you go on taking a set of remedies when they don't make you feel better? Although you need to persevere with the remedies, especially when the condition being treated is deep-rooted or chronic, mistakes are made, and it may be that you would be better off switching to another remedy or group of remedies. The rule of thumb is to continue taking a prescription for at least two weeks and then review the situation. If there has been some improvement, however slight, it is worth going on with the current treatment, although you might want to add other remedies to it in the light of your experiences. If there has been no change at all, or even a worsening of the situation, then you definitely need to take another look at the remedies you are using.

If you do go on taking the remedies after the problem you are treating has gone, you will not be doing yourself any harm, since it is impossible to overdose on the remedies. But equally there will not be any benefit. This means, for example, that there is no point taking gentian every day just in case you feel discouraged next week – the remedies don't work like that. They can't wash away a negative mental state that doesn't yet exist. If you are worried that you might get discouraged, you might be better off taking a remedy against the worrying thoughts (white chestnut, perhaps, or heather if the worries are self-obsessed), as this is the mental state you are in at the moment.

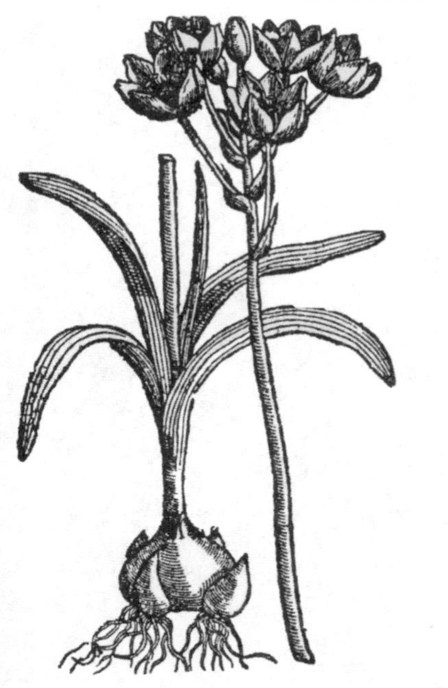

G*enerally you should try to keep the number of different remedies being taken at any one time to six or less. In practice, if you are taking more than this it indicates that you have not thought deeply enough about the underlying emotional states you are dealing with. Prescribing techniques are covered in full in chapters 6 and 7.*

CHAPTER 4

THE THIRTY-EIGHT REMEDIES

In this chapter you will find descriptions of all thirty-eight of the flower remedies and the emotional states that they are used to treat. To make it easier for you to determine which remedies to use, an attempt has been made to indicate the main symptoms and associated health problems that you might expect to find in each case. It is important to remember, however, that a single symptom may have many causes, and that the remedies are most effective when they are selected following careful and sensitive appraisal of the individual personality you are dealing with (see chapter 7).

This chapter can be used in conjunction with chapter 8, where everyday problems are listed along with suggested remedies for each one, and with chapters 9, 10 and 11, which deal with problems specific to women, men and children respectively. If you are looking for help with problems to do with sexuality or relationships generally, you will also find some helpful indications in chapter 13.

Stock bottles of all of the remedies described here can be obtained from reputable health and health food shops.

AGRIMONY

(*Agrimonia eupatoria* or *Agrimonia odorata*)

The agrimony plant is commonly found in hedgerows and fields and waste areas all over the UK. It is a dark green herbaceous perennial with yellow flowers on long slender spikes, blooming from June to August and growing up to about 1 metre high.

PREPARATION: By the sun method.

INDICATIONS: Agrimony is for people who tend to hide their anxieties and worries behind a facade of cheerfulness. They have a great sense of

D*o not confuse the agrimony used for the remedies with the rare fragrant agrimony (*Agrimonia procera*). You can tell fragrant agrimony by its larger, more aromatic flowers and by the fact that its fruit is smooth and ungrooved.*

humour and are always laughing and joking, even in the most trying of circumstances. Indeed, this can be the key to pinpointing the existence of some underlying problem, since when the high spirits persist at inappropriate times it can be a sign that the person is unable to cope with the darker side of life – disappointments, setbacks and so on – and so tries to ignore unpleasant facts in the hope that they will go away. The normal reaction to losing a job or the break-up of a relationship is to feel dejected or upset, but a person for whom agrimony is the indicated remedy will try to pretend that everything is all right and that it doesn't really matter, while all the time the hurt and anguish are pushed deep down inside where nobody can see them.

Agrimony people tend to seek out company and can turn to drink and other artificial thrills in the attempt to drown out the churning thoughts in their heads. At all costs they want to avoid being left alone with their thoughts. Late at night, when all their defences are down, their repressed fears can lead to insomnia and leave the naturally ebullient individual tired and strained.

The agrimony state can affect people of all ages, but *children in particular can be especially susceptible, since there is so much that can appear strange and threatening to them, while at the same time parents

Remember when giving remedies to children that stock bottles contain a large proportion of pure brandy. For this reason you should follow the treatment instructions in chapter 3, and if possible always give the remedies diluted in water.
For the same reason, only diluted remedies should be given to anyone suffering from alcoholism. See chapter 3, and if in doubt consult a medical practitioner.

…rather too inclined to tell them to get on with things …ing a fuss. This can lead them to conceal their worries …r cheerful and normal so as to please the adult world. …y continues, however, and may grow out of all proportion …reated.

The agrimony remedy is given to put people of this type, and anyone suffering from a temporary agrimony state, back in touch with their hidden worries and fears, so helping to reunify their personalities. Once their hidden fears have been faced they can be seen in a truer perspective and, weighed against the great gift for laughter and simplicity that the agrimony type has, they seem to shrink to nothing. The remedy helps the person to laugh at anxieties that have been overcome and understood, rather than go on using laughter as a barrier to prevent self-knowledge.

CASE HISTORY: *Ruth was having trouble sleeping at nights, because her worries would surface then, but she felt obliged to put a brave face on things for the sake of her young family. Agrimony was indicated to help her face her worries full on rather than hiding her real feelings, and larch for the secret lack of self-confidence that she had admitted. She persevered through three treatment bottles before she reported a real improvement.*

KEY SYMPTOMS: A mask of cheerfulness and good humour. Hidden worries and fears. Refusal to face the darker side of life.

ASSOCIATED PROBLEMS: Sleeplessness and restlessness. Tendency to alcohol, nicotine and drug abuse and other risky, thrill-seeking behaviour. Tiredness.

TREATMENT GOALS: Restore the ability to cope with the bad and the good in life. Allow the person to see problems clearly and in perspective. Bring a deeper, calmer, quieter joy.

ASPEN

(*Populus tremula*)

The aspen is a kind of poplar well known for its catkins and its tremulous dark green leaves, which quiver in the faintest breath of air. A slender tree, it grows up to about 26 metres high and is quite common throughout Britain and the rest of Europe. The tree is in bloom in March and April, until the catkins wither and the slightly sticky buds burst into leaf.

PREPARATION: By the boiling method.

INDICATIONS: Aspen is the remedy for people who suffer from vague fears and apprehensions. These are not fears with any definite cause; rather they are the kind that creep up on the sufferer without warning and for no apparent reason. At the milder end of the scale there are forebodings of the type that make you say, 'I think that something awful is going to happen'; but the fear can also be intense, verging on panic, and may be accompanied at times by physical symptoms such as trembling and sweating.

Sometimes the aspen fear is a fear of the unknown – triggered by thoughts of death or religious anguish, perhaps – and it often strikes when the person is alone. In any case, it is almost invariably faced alone, because even if the sufferer is with close friends or family members during an attack the tendency is not to say anything about it to anyone as there is no rational explanation to offer and the person may be scared of being thought weak, or even of being laughed at.

People who are in severe emotional or mental distress should speak to a qualified counsellor or health practitioner if this is appropriate.

Because the fear is so vague it is hard for the sufferer to find a solution to it – it seems as if nothing can be done. This can lead to feelings of hopelessness and frustration and of course to the fear that the attacks will return: the fear of being afraid.

Sometimes the attacks come at night, with the person waking up in a cold sweat as if from a bad dream. People in this state may complain of half-remembered nightmares or may take to sleepwalking, almost as if they are trying to run away from their fear while they sleep. They may also be afraid of the dark or become superstitious about animals and places.

In really serious cases the person may suffer from delusions and feelings of persecution and paranoia – the feeling that 'they' are out to get you. This state of mind with its irrational suspicion might also indicate the need for holly, while the lack of mental control might suggest that cherry plum could help. But you should also be aware that with extreme states of mind like this the person may be suffering from and be under treatment for a specific *mental illness.

When given to people suffering from such ill-defined fears, aspen helps restore confidence in the powers of good and the fundamental spiritual health of the world. As the anxiety fades, the heightened receptivity that made these people so open to irrational fears is not lost; instead, it is redirected into more positive channels so that they can use their wonderful gifts of empathy and spirituality for good.

In the case of mental illness, as with any other illness, you should never encourage or instruct someone to stop taking medication that has been prescribed for him or her by a qualified medical practitioner. The flower remedies can be used in conjunction with any other form of therapy, and their efficacy will not harm or be harmed by the presence of other types of treatment, whether based on drugs or counselling.

CASE HISTORY: *After starting a new job, Marie suffered from a constant feeling of dread and anxiety, as if something awful was about to happen, but she couldn't think what might be* *causing this. Relationships with her new colleagues seemed to be civil enough, and she enjoyed the job itself.*

Aspen alone was indicated. Marie took it for three weeks, during which time there was continuous improvement. As the remedy did its work she realized that her feelings were centred on the building where she worked, which was a converted abattoir. A committed vegetarian, she had unconsciously been dwelling on its former role and allowing that to influence her state of mind.

In place of aspen, walnut was now given to help her shake off the influence the building had over her, and this finally resolved her problem.

As this case shows, aspen can on occasion help to put a name to a fear that has so far been nameless. Once something has been named it is often easier to deal with it.

KEY SYMPTOMS: Unexplained anxiety, fear and terror. Forebodings that 'something' is going to happen.

ASSOCIATED PROBLEMS: Nightmares. Fear of dreams and the dark. Palpitations, sweating, gooseflesh and trembling. Superstitious fears and an overactive imagination.

TREATMENT GOALS: Provide reassurance that there is nothing to be scared of. Give the person the confidence to explore religious thoughts without fear.

BEECH

(*Fagus sylvatica*)

The thin, smooth, silver-grey bark of the beech tree can be seen in many parts of Europe. It grows up to 30 metres high, and both male and female flowers appear on the same tree from early April to the end of May. The male flowers can be identified by the way they hang down like pompons; the

female flowers are held in a sort of cup which later forms the beech-nut.
PREPARATION: By the boiling method.
INDICATIONS: Beech types are characterized by being intolerant of other people's faults. Proud and tending to irritability, they never give others the benefit of the doubt and tend to be very narrow-minded. Above all, they are unable to put themselves in the place of others. They don't stop to think about the disadvantages of birth or education that some people may have had to overcome, and of the corresponding good fortune in their own circumstances – instead, they only look at people's shortcomings and pronounce the harshest of judgements. The caricature beech person is the peppery retired gentleman who can't understand why unemployed people don't buck their ideas up and get a job, or the narrow-minded housewife who criticizes the cheap clothes worn by her neighbour's children, without pausing to consider the difference between the two family incomes, or the fact that her neighbour has three children to clothe while she has only one.

The result of so much arrogance and such a lack of humility and fellow feeling is that the beech person can end up feeling very lonely and cut off from the society of 'ordinary' people. Although the beech type may say that this is fine and that common people are stupid and not worth knowing, in fact there can in extreme cases be a real desperation at the lack of human companionship, especially as, to the beech person, the way of life that other people do not adhere to seems unquestionably right and self-evidently superior.

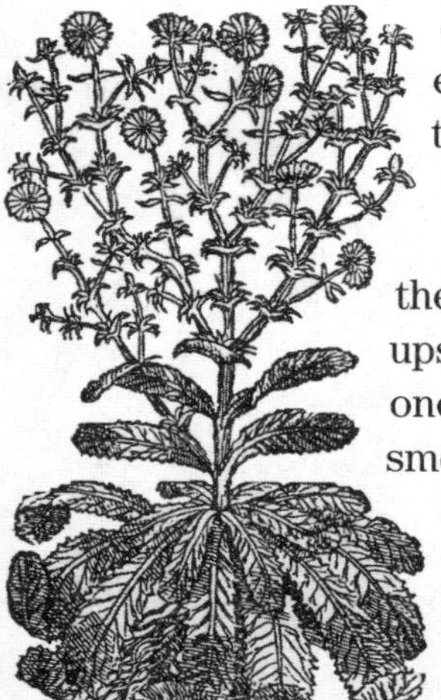

Faced with what they see as wilful stupidity on the part of other people, beech types tend to become upset over the merest trifles. The beech person is the one who says 'I can't stand the way she always smoothes down her skirt' or 'He always says "Hi" instead of "Hello" and it drives me crazy.' The violence of their response is out of all proportion to the behaviour complained of. Because they are so often irritated and impatient, beech types have a tendency to be very tense and highly strung.

The beech remedy is given to allow these people to relax a little and see the good in others instead of launching into condemnation. Once they realize that people can be different, adhere to different standards and follow different paths in life, yet still be worthy of praise and love instead of censure, beech types can begin to look at their own attitudes and beliefs with a clearer mind, treating themselves with the same tolerance that they now display to others.

Beech people have the potential for true insight because of their highly developed critical and diagnostic faculties. Once the remedy has restored their sense of balance and unity, they can begin to use their gifts in a constructive way. This is why well-balanced beech people can make excellent counsellors and healers.

CASE HISTORY: *Vera, a spinster in her fifties, complained of feeling tired all the time. This was interfering with her usual round of what she called 'good works', such as helping out at jumble sales. She made a point of saying that she only helped 'deserving' causes, and was rather proud of the fact that she had recently refused to support a housing charity; in her opinion the people it helped had brought their troubles upon themselves.*

Instead of vervain, which her strong involvement in charity work might have suggested, beech was indicated as her type remedy because of her intolerance. To help her regain her strength olive was added.

A few weeks later Vera reported that she was much happier and was getting on better with all types of people.

Key symptoms: Lack of understanding. Intolerance and irritability. Narrow-minded refusal to see the positive potential in people and situations.

Associated problems: Tension. Loneliness and isolation.

Treatment goals: Restore balance and widen mental horizons. Increase empathy with other people's situations and beliefs. Encourage greater humility and sense of unity.

CENTAURY

(*Centaurium umbellatum*)

Centaury is an annual plant whose small, pink flowers appear in June, July and August. It is easy to spot centaury because the flowers are shaped like five-pointed stars, and appear all bunched together at the end of a much-divided stem. The plant favours dry areas and wasteland. It grows up to 45 centimetres high, depending on the local soil and conditions.

Preparation: By the sun method.

Indications: The people who need centaury are those who have turned a willingness to serve others into a vice, because the way they accept being led and ordered about only encourages other people to be domineering and tyrannical. Lacking the strength to say no and seeming to invite dominance, they could be thought of as the willing victims of a form of emotional vampirism practised by stronger people – chicory and vine types, for example.

The plant used for the remedies is the common centaury. Be particularly careful not to use perennial centaury (Centaurium scilloides), which has larger flowers and a non-flowering stem, or the slender centaury (Centaurium tenuiflorum), as both of these are becoming increasingly rare.

Like the victims of a vampire, centaury people are often pale, listless and tired, as if all the life force has been drawn out of them. This physical condition is in no way the result of their being naturally lazy, but rather is caused by their overexerting themselves in the service of others. Their physical tiredness also stands in stark contrast to their often pronounced mental alertness.

Centaury types are those who sacrifice their own lives to satisfy the needs or opinions of others. The middle-aged woman caring for an infirm relative at the cost of starting her own family is a classic example of this. Others include the son studying law to please his parents, when his real inclinations draw him towards chemistry or computer science; and the grandmother giving up her own social life to sit in baby-sitting five nights a week. Instead of willing friends and helpers, centaury types quickly become slaves. Because they are so much taken for granted by their exploiters they seem to lose their own personalities entirely, allowing themselves to be swayed by prevailing social conventions and worries about what other people might think.

People recovering from illness can sometimes fall into a temporary centaury state when they feel too tired and worn out to think for themselves, and so willingly accede to whatever is asked of them.

Given to anyone who is in the state described, the centaury remedy helps to boost the victim's life force. Sufferers will find the strength to redefine their own personalities on their own terms and when necessary to say 'no', politely, firmly and with love. A new freedom from the stifling bonds of servitude is discovered and the former 'slaves' are able to offer help and care to others from a position of equality rather than one of subservience. When the remedy has completed its work the great gift of devotion to a just cause can be exercised properly, since the person will be in a position to choose a true path rather than drifting along helplessly according to the dictates of the first strong personality to come along.

CASE HISTORY: *Laura had three children, all under the age of ten, who were sleeping very badly. She was exhausted from having to get up to them at all hours of the night and had been diagnosed as anaemic.*

It soon emerged that when the children woke at night Laura's husband always woke her up to go and see to them, even if he hadn't gone to bed yet. She seemed just to accept this and found it difficult to say 'no' to her husband, so centaury was recommended to help her overcome her subservience, together with olive for the physical tiredness.

A few months later Laura reported that soon after starting with the remedies she had talked to her husband and told him how unreasonable he was being. He was now taking on his fair share of responsibility for settling the children and she was less tired. The anaemia was improving too, enabling Laura to reduce the number of iron tablets she was taking.

KEY SYMPTOMS: Lack of will-power. Inability to say no. Enslavement to convention and to the beliefs and desires of more forceful personalities.
ASSOCIATED PROBLEMS: Tiredness and exhaustion. Frustration caused by lack of inner strength, personal direction and achievement. Easily influenced by the views and attitudes of stronger personalities.
TREATMENT GOALS: Restore the ability to make reasoned, free choices. Nurture the personality. Provide strength to follow one's true path in life.

CERATO

(*Ceratostigma willmottiana*)

Cerato is a little different from most of the flower remedies, in that it is not native to Britain, but comes from the Himalayas and China. This deciduous shrub grows up to 1.25 metres high, and because it is not a wild flower is only to be found in cultivated gardens. The delicate blue flowers appear in tightly packed clusters, blooming in August and September.

PREPARATION: By the sun method.

INDICATIONS: This is the remedy for people who are incapable of trusting their own judgement. It's not that they cannot decide anything at all, or that they make bad decisions – often in fact their decisions are very good and at heart they can hold very definite opinions – it's just that they think the answers they find by themselves are too simple or too intuitive to be correct.

Cerato is the only remedy that is prepared from cultivated plants. In all other cases the plants used are wild, growing where and how they will, free from human interference.

At bottom the problem with cerato people is that they distrust themselves and their beliefs. Consequently they are always running to other people to ask what they would do in such and such a case. Because the advice they receive is often flawed, they can look rather foolish when they choose an inappropriate course of action and end up doing or saying something that they would never have done or said if they had trusted themselves. And because they apply to so many different people for advice, they are forever changing their minds, as they tend to believe and accept the last thing they were told.

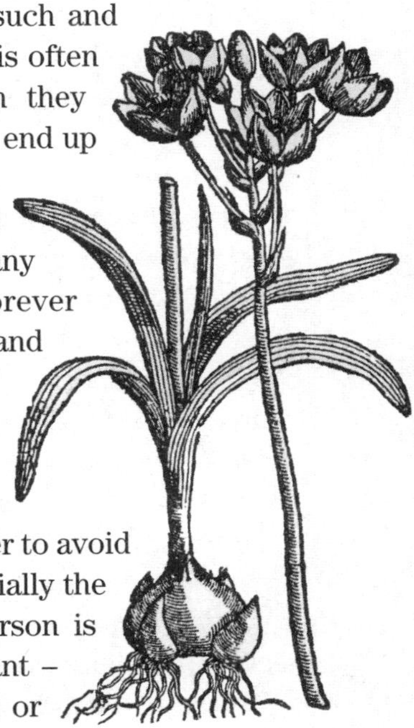

Cerato people are often very talkative, so much so that others can find them wearing and tiresome. In extreme cases other people may deliberately avoid the cerato type, in order to avoid the endless stream of questions. This is especially the case when the problems that the cerato person is trying to deal with are trivial and unimportant – what shoes to buy, for example, or whether or not to try the latest diet, haircut or fashion.

As if in an attempt to make up for their own changeability, cerato types can show a real and sometimes exaggerated respect for those who seem to be able to make up their minds without difficulty. For this reason they are easily seduced into adopting extreme causes and following charismatic leaders. They may even copy the behaviour and mannerisms of a forceful character in a soap opera or a film: the normally hesitant teenager who strides out of a cinema in imitation of the fictional hero he has just been watching may well be a cerato type. But they make very poor followers and inconstant mimics, since they will change tack the very next time they obtain a new opinion.

The cerato remedy given to people in this state helps them to trust their intuition. Because intuition is often highly developed in cerato types, this is an entirely positive move. As their judgements are proved right over and over again they will gain in confidence, so that they will be able to reject the bad advice offered by some and will not need to go around unnecessarily soliciting advice from others.

CASE HISTORY: *Brenda had been offered a major promotion at work, but if she accepted it she would have to move to London, where she had no friends and few relations.*

She had two weeks to decide. Although her immediate inclination was to take the job, she wasted valuable time asking the advice of all and sundry. Some told her to stay, others to move, and one person told her to try taking cerato so that she could make up her own mind.

Fortunately Brenda took this last piece of advice, and was soon flat-hunting in London.

KEY SYMPTOMS: Lack of faith in one's intuition. Constantly and unnecessarily seeking advice. Distrust of one's own judgement.
ASSOCIATED PROBLEMS: Overtalkative. Can appear foolish or silly. Sense

of identity weakened by imitation of more forceful types.
Treatment goals: Restore confidence in one's own intuition and judgement. Grant the sufferer a quiet, unobtrusive assurance.

CHERRY PLUM

(*Prunus cerasifera*)

The cherry plum is named after its deep red-purple fruit, which does look rather like a small plum. This small tree can grow up to about 7.5 metres high, although it is often pruned short and planted to form hedgerows and windbreaks. The white flowers appear from February to March, either singly or in clusters gathered on a single twig.
Preparation: By the boiling method.
Indications: The cherry plum state is an extreme one at its worst, for sufferers can feel they are losing control of their minds. They feel they are going insane, and may fly into murderous rages when they want to attack other people. In other cases the violence is directed against themselves; they want to commit *suicide to put an end to the extreme despair and hopelessness they feel.

More often, the cherry plum state is a form of fear: the fear of going mad and of committing some unforgiveable act, whether directed against others or against the sufferer. This fear often comes at the end of a prolonged period of mental, emotional or physical strain which has worn the person down, and the mild form of hysteria that results may in time lead to a genuine nervous breakdown. Although it is almost

Anyone who is talking about suicide or any other violent act should be taken seriously. Such people should seek the advice of a doctor, psychiatrist or other counsellor at the earliest opportunity.

as intense, it is a different fear from the sheer terror of the rock rose state, for while the latter is usually clear for all to see, people in the cherry plum state may well do a fairly good job of covering up their fear – in fact, they will try very hard to do so, since giving way is precisely what they are most frightened of.

Because cherry plum is the remedy for the loss of mental control, it can also be used to treat moods that result in similar feelings. For example, it may help deal with a young *child's violent temper tantrum, with all its associated kicking, stamping and screaming. In its own way, the overwhelming emotions felt by a child in this state are as strong as the more adult and more frightening version described above. In both cases it is the complete loss of rationality and self-control that make cherry plum the indicated remedy.

In all these situations the action of the remedy is the same. It helps to replace anxiety with calm, and in place of unreasoning hysteria instils a quiet rationality. The result aimed at is a whole new level of sanity, only to be attained by those who have looked into the abyss and have turned away, made stronger by the experience.

W*hen giving remedies to children remember that the stock concentrate is mostly pure brandy. Follow the treatment instructions in chapter 3, and if possible always give the remedies diluted in water.*

CASE HISTORY: *Francis was an elm type, always prepared to take on responsibility and deal with it capably. Following the death of his eldest son in a car crash, however, he fell into a deep depression during which he would fly into a rage at the slightest provocation, blaming himself and those around him for what had happened. Because of his uncontrolled rage and the fact that* *his thoughts had been turning suicidal, Francis was given cherry plum as well as his type remedy elm. Sweet chestnut was used too, for the ultimate despair that the loss of a loved one can bring, and finally star of Bethlehem for the shock.*

Recovery was of course very slow, but the remedies did turn Francis away from harming himself, allowing time for his natural recuperative powers to come into play. He soon realized that he owed it to the rest of his family to be strong and cope with his grief rather than give in to it.

KEY SYMPTOMS: Desperation caused by fear of going insane. Fear of hurting others or of committing suicide.
ASSOCIATED PROBLEMS: Hysteria. Uncontrolled rages.
TREATMENT GOALS: Restore inner peace. Remove fear. Restore control over mind and emotions.

CHESTNUT BUD

(*Aesculus hippocastanum*)

The white (or horse) chestnut, which grows up to 30 metres high, provides two remedies: chestnut bud and white chestnut. While the bark on the trunk and the sturdy main branches is grey-brown and scaly, the smaller twigs holding the sticky buds are smooth in winter; the buds themselves are used to make the chestnut bud remedy.

PREPARATION: By the boiling method, when the swollen ends of the buds have started to burst open.

INDICATIONS: Most of us learn from our mistakes, and many can avoid mistakes altogether by seeing what happens to other people. However, some people seem to go on making the same mistakes over and over again, never learning from their experiences.

There can be many reasons for this failure to learn. Some people don't pay enough attention to what they are doing and act thoughtlessly. Others

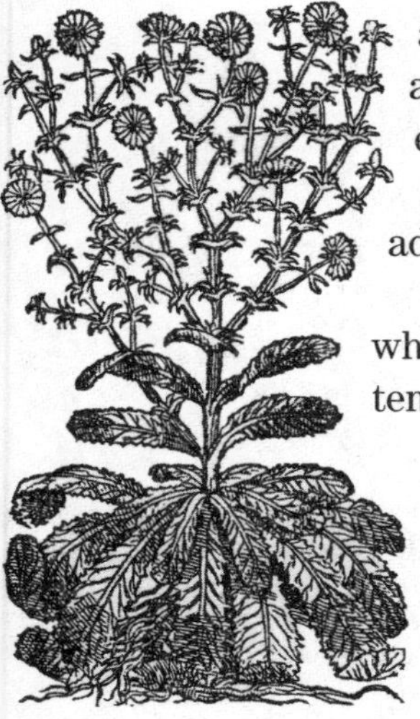

are simply in too much of a hurry. Still others seem actively to welcome each repetition as a new experience, and only after it has ended in just the same way do they realize that it was just an old adventure revisited.

Chestnut bud is the remedy for all these people, whether theirs is a semi-permanent condition or a temporary state.

Long-term chestnut bud types are generally people who find it all too easy to forget the past. In itself this is no bad thing, since being able to let go of the past is a necessary prerequisite to advancing in life. But while it may be good to forget past mistakes it is also important to be able to remember the lessons of life. Chestnut bud people are unable to do this until they have gone through an experience several times: they are those who change a job they don't like for another of the same type, or form a long series of unsatisfactory relationships with people who, to any outside observer, seem to have come from the same mould. On a more mundane level, they may have the same haircut every time they go to the hairdressers and be surprised each time that it doesn't suit them, or go on reading late at night despite the fact that they always suffer from headaches the next day. As this last example suggests, chestnut bud people may be prone to recurring minor ailments such as colds, sore throats, hay fever, upset stomachs or general fatigue, and in all cases the root of this will be found in some avoidable circumstance that they go on repeating even though they know it will make them ill yet again.

Those who might fall temporarily into this category include children and adolescents who sometimes go through periods of inattention during which they repeat the same, often trivial mistakes, however many reminders they are given. In this case you need to be careful to differentiate between the failure to learn of the true chestnut bud type and the lack of attention caused by day-dreaming and fantasizing about the future, typical of clematis people and of many *young people in particular.

Older people can also fall into a temporary chestnut bud state when they fail to pay attention to what they are doing. Here too it is important to watch out for an easy mistake in prescribing, which involves confusing chestnut bud and honeysuckle types. Although both types are singled out for being inattentive, there is a simple test to tell them apart: while the chestnut bud forgets the past almost at once, the honeysuckle lives in the past in order to forget the present.

Always follow the treatment instructions in chapter 3, especially when giving the remedies to young children, since the undiluted stock bottles contain almost pure brandy.

People who need the chestnut bud remedy are not as a rule particularly upset or distressed by their condition, so this is not such a dramatic state as some others. However, they do risk falling into a kind of stagnation because they are unable to progress as quickly or positively as they should. Involved in endless repetition of old mistakes, they can easily miss real opportunities and potentially fulfilling experiences.

The remedy is given to people in this state to help them see themselves and their mistakes more clearly. This allows them to gather their scattered experiences into firm principles so that they can move on to a new stage in their development, learning all the time and profiting from what they learn.

Case history: *Polly was thirty when she began to suffer from migraines and depression. She was unhappy in her routine secretarial job, but couldn't decide what else to do, although she was considering a slightly better paid position in another office.*

In the previous ten years she had had eight separate but similar jobs.

It seemed that Polly was about to move to yet another job she wouldn't enjoy. The inability to learn from previous experience indicated chestnut bud, to which wild oat was added since she expressed a desire to do something worthwhile with her life but couldn't decide which direction to take.

A few months later we heard that Polly had enrolled on a part-time course to train as a legal secretary. She had decided to stay in her current job, as it gave her more time to study, and had been migraine-free for the past six weeks.

KEY SYMPTOMS: Inability to learn from experience. Thoughtless repetition of past mistakes. Failure to move on.

ASSOCIATED PROBLEMS: Absent-mindedness and forgetfulness. Periodic bouts of preventable illness.

TREATMENT GOALS: Focus the mind on the present so that lessons can be learnt. Encourage an objective view of events. Encourage a sense of real progression and achievement.

CHICORY

(*Cichorium intybus*)

The chicory is a perennial plant with a strong, very upright, grooved and bristly stem. At the base a rosette of hairy, toothed leaves spreads out across the ground, while further up the leaves are smaller and pointed. Chicory flowers throughout the mid to late summer, a few clusters of bright blue-violet blooms budding out from the stem and then fading, to be replaced by others.

It is found in waste areas, and is especially fond of gravelly and chalky soil.

PREPARATION: By the sun method.

INDICATIONS: Chicory people are usually possessive in their personal relationships. The aged parent who uses his or her infirmity to keep a child unmarried and at home is a common example, but there is just as much of a chicory state in those children who insist on always being the centre of attention and who use tears, smiles, temper and sweetness with complete indifference in order to get their way. In both cases the desire to be loved by other people has manifested itself in an attempt to trap them.

As both these examples show, there is often a great deal of cunning, conscious or unconscious, in the chicory mentality, and deceit is practised as a matter of course. While they are easily hurt by what they consider to be rejections or snubs, chicory types can just as easily mimic the hurt and magnify perfectly normal, reasonable behaviour into the basest treachery. They are fond of recalling, loudly and at length, all the sacrifices they have made for their ungrateful spouses, children, parents or friends, contrasting their selfless care for others with the terrible selfishness of others towards them. The word 'duty' comes easily to their lips, although it is never the duty to live and let live, and they generally do all they can to keep loved ones near at hand and under complete control.

People of this type may seem to have more love and care to offer than others. They can make a great deal of fuss over their victims and seem to take an exaggerated interest in their well-being. But theirs is an intrusive and uncomfortable sort of care to receive: attention forced on the recipient rather than freely offered and received. And of course there is always the half-hidden reproach: 'How can you leave me alone when all I care about is you?'

What has happened is that the natural outward flow of such people's love has been blocked so that it all washes back towards the source. They quite literally fall in love with themselves, with all the attendant feelings of self-regard, self-pity and selfishness that this implies. But in fact self-regard is accompanied by low self-esteem, and chicory types are often lonely or afraid of being left alone. They may feel genuinely unloved and unlovable, and this is why they need the constant declarations of love, regard and gratitude that they work so hard to elicit.

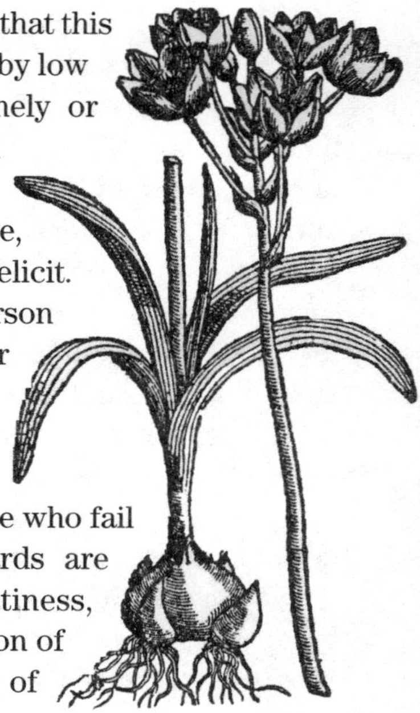

The watchful cunning that the chicory person uses in personal relationships often spills over into other areas of life where there would seem to be no connection. For this reason, people of this type can seem to adopt very high standards and be rather severe about those who fail to meet them. However, their high standards are usually no more than fussiness and pettiness, designed simply to put other people in a position of weakness and keep themselves at the centre of attention.

The chicory remedy serves to remove the blockage to the normal flow of love. Sufferers are able to give care and attention to others without thinking of the cost. In return they receive genuine gratitude and love, and the vicious circle of manipulator and manipulated is broken.

CASE HISTORY: *To himself Darren seemed the most likeable of people, forever visiting friends or inviting them to dinner. But no one showed any gratitude.*

His marriage had ended the previous year and he spoke of all the attentions he had heaped on his wife, to no avail. He was also resentful that his children didn't want to spend every weekend with him. To add to his misery, he was suffering from a persistent rash.

Chicory was prescribed for Darren's self-centred desire to manipulate his loved ones by overwhelming them. Crab apple was added as a cleanser for the rash and to counteract his self-

dislike. He was also advised to try Rescue Remedy cream to soothe his skin (see chapter 5).

The rash cleared up surprisingly quickly and within a few weeks Darren was getting on much better with his ex-wife. And now that he had stopped pestering his children to visit him they were coming more often of their own accord.

KEY SYMPTOMS: Possessiveness. Selfishness. Desire to control the lives and behaviour of others, especially loved ones. Need to be the centre of attention.

ASSOCIATED PROBLEMS: Fussy about trivialities. Argumentative, deceitful and manipulative. Prone to hysterical illness and hypochondria. Loneliness and low self-esteem.

TREATMENT GOALS: Encourage selflessness. Grant the security needed to give love without expecting a return.

CLEMATIS

(*Clematis vitalba*)

Clematis is a perennial climber usually found growing over hedges and thickets and anywhere where there is chalky soil. The leaves grow up to 20 centimetres long, and are large in comparison with the green-white flowers that appear from July to September. When the flowers are fully mature, the sepals in the heads curve down and turn grey – hence the common name of old man's beard.

PREPARATION: By the sun method.

INDICATIONS: There are several remedies for people who do not pay enough attention to the things and people around them. Honeysuckle, for example, is for those who live in the past, while white chestnut is for those who find the present swamped by persistent worries and nagging thoughts. Clematis too is a remedy for inattention, although in this case the cause is not worry or nostalgia but rather day-

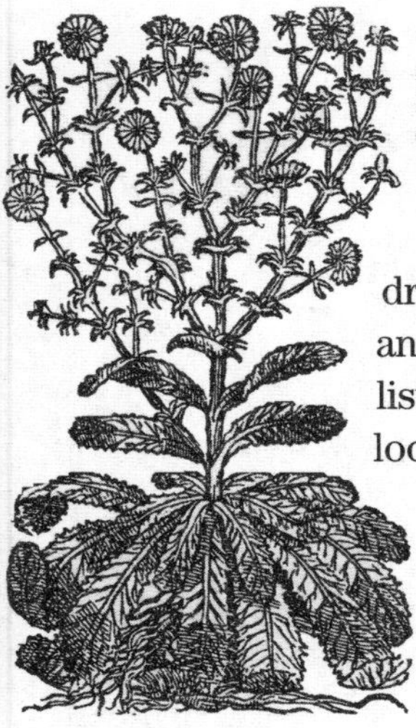

dreaming, for clematis people are those who seem to live in the future instead of the present, and who escape present unpleasantness or boredom by drifting off into a world of fantasy.

The clematis state is characterized by a vacant, dreamy look and a rather absent-minded indifference, and clematis people prefer to be alone. Where others listen, the clematis type barely hears; where others look, the clematis person only sees; where others make efforts to notice their surroundings, the clematis doesn't think to try. Typically such people may be inclined to suffer from problems with their hearing or their other senses, and their memories are poor because they are so rarely used.

People of this type seem to drift through life as if it isn't of much interest to them. This characteristic can become rather dangerous when there is illness, for clematis people are neither passionate nor fighters, and the most difficult part of treating them can be to make them interested enough to try to get better. Dr Bach went so far as to say that their lack of interest in getting better could amount to 'a polite form of suicide': they are the type of people who don't go out in a blaze of glory but rather just fade away through lack of commitment.

Clematis people are generally listless and drowsy and are prone to *faintness and giddiness. You will rarely find them suffering from insomnia, for they find it easy to fall asleep at any time, even on occasions when it is most inappropriate – at dinner, perhaps, or in a cinema. They can sleep through any noise and disturbance and once they are asleep it takes a great deal to rouse them.

Persistent giddiness and faintness can be caused by a number of physical conditions, some of them serious. If in doubt about any physical symptoms you should always consult a qualified medical practitioner.

As you might expect, since they are so closely in touch with their own unconscious, clematis people can be artistically or spiritually gifted. In the negative state their potential is often unrealized, however, since they find it all too easy to build castles in the air instead of laying bricks and mortar in the real world. Not only can the clematis remedy help to bring people in this condition back to earth and restore their interest in the present, it can also give them the practical desire they need to actually seize hold of their dreams and turn them into reality. Instead of simply dreaming of a better future tomorrow, they are able to work in a purposeful way to build one today.

CASE HISTORY: *Six-year-old Naomi was listless and would fall asleep at all hours of the day and night, sometimes even while people were talking to her. In conversation she was inattentive and prone to day-dreaming. She had a good imagination, however; her favourite game was 'pretending'. Accordingly, clematis was indicated as her type remedy.*

As with most children, Naomi responded well and quickly grew livelier, taking more interest in school and in life generally. She didn't stop her fantasizing, but was better able to integrate her dreams with real life and so get more out of both.

KEY SYMPTOMS: Day-dreaming and fantasizing. Lack of interest in present reality. Poor will to live.
ASSOCIATED PROBLEMS: Sleepiness, giddiness and tendency to faintness. Absent-mindedness and forgetfulness.
TREATMENT GOALS: Restore interest in the present. Give an outer purpose to artistic and sensitive inner life.

Always follow the treatment instructions in chapter 3, especially when giving the remedies to young children, since the undiluted stock bottles contain almost pure brandy.

CRAB APPLE

(*Malus pumila or Malus sylvestris*)

The deciduous crab apple tree grows in hedges and woodland. It is about 7.5 metres high, low-branched with a twisted trunk, and in late spring is covered in clusters of pink-white flowers. Together with a few leaves, these grow at the end of short spurs jutting out of the long brown shoots.

PREPARATION: By the boiling method, when the dark rose-coloured buds have just opened (late April to May).

INDICATIONS: All of us at some stage in our lives find there is something about ourselves that we don't like. For some, this may be connected with an action that is regretted, such as having spoken sharply to a friend or having done something mean and petty. Others have a habit that they can't stop but which disgusts them, such as smoking or overeating. Still others might have a physical feature or blemish that preys on their minds, like a spot, a wart or a boil. And sometimes perfectly 'ordinary' sickness can make us feel dirty, so that a simple cold or stomach upset becomes magnified out of all proportion and seems to turn into a major problem.

In all these cases, crab apple is given to cleanse the mind and body. It is the remedy for all feelings of self-disgust, and for the despair and despondency that self-disgust leads to.

In a similar way, crab apple can be used to cleanse the mind of unwanted, obsessive thoughts. People who forget the thousands they owe while they carefully count the small change in their pockets might benefit from the crab apple remedy,

as might the mother who worries over a torn pair of mittens before she attends to her child's bleeding hands. Anyone who shows signs of becoming fixated on one aspect of a situation to the exclusion of all others can be helped by the cleansing remedy.

Often the cause of disgust is purely psychological. Frigidity, anorexia and phobias – particularly those directed against rats, insects, germs and other 'unclean' things – all involve an element of the crab apple state, since the feeling of uncleanness and self-loathing is present in all three. Watch out too for compulsive behaviour such as the continual washing of hands, or re-checking the same thing over and over again, or obsessive counting. All these may indicate the need for crab apple to wash away the accumulated psychological dirt.

Crab apple can also be used where there is a real physical reason for the feeling of uncleanliness. For example, people working in hospitals might feel the need to use it when they have been working in conditions of infection and disease, and the remedy can be applied externally to cuts and grazes where there is fear of dirt having got into the wound.

The action of crab apple is to purify and restore mind, spirit and body. Sufferers are able to see things in proportion once again, and the feelings of despondency and shame they felt when they were unwell are washed away. Crab apple allows people to regain control over their thoughts and, most importantly, lets them begin to like themselves once more.

When used against real uncleanliness, crab apple washes the body clean while strengthening the mind against the fear of infection. The natural defences are left free to do their work of maintaining bodily health, untrammelled by unhelpful feelings of disgust.

CASE HISTORY: *Brigitte was twelve years old, and a keen ballet dancer. She was preparing for an exhibition in which she was to be the principal dancer. But then she began to say she was ugly and couldn't dance.*

Crab apple was given for Brigitte's feelings of self-dislike. Her doubts about her ability dated from the time she was given the lead in the exhibition, so elm was added for the lack of confidence rather than larch, because this was a temporary crisis and she was normally a confident child.

Brigitte responded well to the remedies and soon began to look forward to her starring role.

KEY SYMPTOMS: Feelings of uncleanliness. Self-disgust and self-loathing. Also called for in cases where there really has been contact with infection or contaminants.

ASSOCIATED PROBLEMS: Phobias. Overfastidious attitude to the physical side of life. Frigidity.

TREATMENT GOALS: Restore sense of proportion. Restore self-respect. Leave the sufferer at ease with his or her own physicality and unworried by illness.

ELM

(*Ulmus procera*)

The tree used to make the elm remedy is the English or common elm - although thanks to the ravages of Dutch elm disease the term 'common' is sadly less appropriate than it once was. Where it is still found, it prefers woods and hedgerows, where it grows to 15-45 metres high.

The trunk is very large and is covered in a cracked grey-brown bark. The oval leaves grow only after the flowers have bloomed in February or March. The small red flowers grow in tight clusters that look a little like dried raspberries.

PREPARATION: Elm is prepared using the boiling method, choosing flowers from as many trees as possible. Avoid those parts of the country where there are only a few elms left.

Indications: Elm people are in many respects very successful human beings, for they are usually doing something worthwhile, and doing it well. Just occasionally the responsibility they have accepted may become a little too much to bear, and they can then easily become downhearted and begin to doubt their own ability to cope. At times like these, elm is indicated to reassure them and give them back their ability to shoulder great burdens without worry or doubt.

Although the classic elm person is someone in a position of great trust and responsibility, such as a doctor, politician or judge, anyone can experience a temporary elm state. This might occur when family responsibilities weigh particularly heavily, or when someone has been given an especially difficult and important job to do at work. It can also be caused by any unexpected setback or criticism which breeds doubt in the person's mind.

The symptoms felt by someone in the elm state can range from tiredness and weakness, through slight depression and worry, to panic and complete exhaustion. In all cases, however, the symptoms are acute (arising suddenly and as quickly dealt with) rather than chronic (developing slowly and lasting a long time). This is because elm people, who are usually capable, intelligent and intuitive, have a calm centre; the knowledge of their own ability usually helps them ride out emotional storms.

The need to treat this state is nevertheless paramount, for many other people rely on the elm person for their own happiness and security. And if minor hiccups can cause distress to others, major breakdowns in elm people can have terrible consequences for their dependants.

Elm helps to restore these people's natural self-confidence in very short order. They respond well to treatment, for they expect to get better, and they soon see that any temporary setbacks are indeed temporary. Restored to health, their great faith in themselves and others comes back all the stronger for having been tested. Because of the way it helps to bring people back to themselves, this remedy has been called smelling-salts for the mind: its action is often just as dramatic.

> **CASE HISTORY:** *George, a partner in a profitable engineering firm, had always been on top of his work until he suffered a minor nervous breakdown. Although he had been assured of a complete recovery, he felt suddenly overwhelmed by all the problems he would have to deal with once he was well again and was considering leaving his beloved business: something he would never normally have contemplated.*
>
> *Elm was prescribed to help George's temporary crisis of confidence . He took it throughout the recovery period and his confidence soon returned.*

KEY SYMPTOMS: Feeling of being overwhelmed by responsibilities that are usually accepted calmly. Temporary loss of self-confidence.
ASSOCIATED PROBLEMS: Exhaustion. Depression.
TREATMENT GOALS: Allow people to get back to their true calling. Restore usual calm judgement and faith in abilities.

GENTIAN

(*Gentianella amarella*)

Gentian is an upright plant that grows in dry conditions such as hill- and cliff-tops. The spearhead-shaped leaves are dark green and grow straight from the stem. The flowers, which appear from August to October, are blue-violet and grow either singly or in clusters all over the plant. Each of the clusters is attached to the stem by a single short stalk.
PREPARATION: Prepare the remedy using the sun method.
INDICATIONS: Gentian is the remedy for people who feel discouraged and despondent whenever

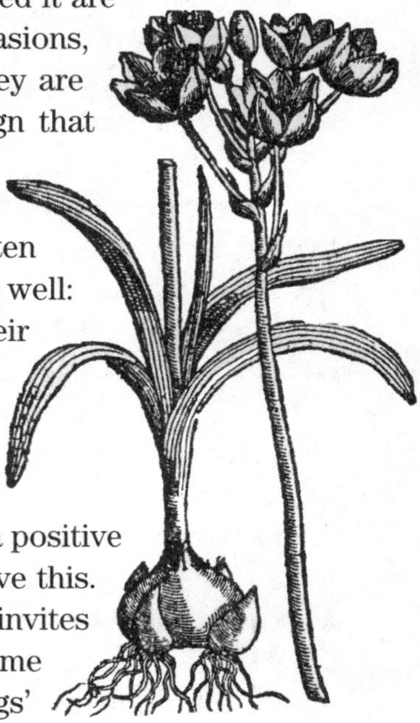

they experience a setback. The people who need it are those who tend to be melancholy on such occasions, and so become doubtful about the future. They are those who take the smallest reversal as a sign that their problems are too much for them and that there is little they can do to find a way through. And they do this despite the fact that very often they are really making progress and getting on well: the temporary setback is enough to awaken their natural pessimism, despite all evidence to the contrary.

While other people may find it easy to see that many of their problems are self-induced and caused by their own inability to maintain a positive state of mind, gentian types simply don't believe this. They don't see that a negative attitude to life invites disappointment and failure. Instead they blame circumstances, their unlucky stars or 'things' generally. Unlike the mustard type's depression, however, there is always a named cause of the problem. The gentian type is never at a loss to give reasons for being depressed.

This is not to suggest that gentian is only used to treat people who don't have good reason to feel downhearted. The named cause may well be unavoidable and very real: failing an exam, redundancy, accidental injury and so on. In all cases, it is the way the person reacts to the setback and how this illuminates his or her personality that indicates which remedy to give. Anyone who feels inclined to throw in the towel at such a setback is a candidate for gentian.

One very common cause of discouragement is physical illness. Gentian people make poor patients, since they are always inclined to give up on a treatment before it has had a chance to help them. For this reason you will often find gentian prescribed to people halfway through a course of treatment involving other flower remedies. When used like this it helps to counteract any doubts and discouragement sufferers might feel because of the time it is taking them to get better. Similarly, it can be used for any temporary setback which leaves people feeling that things are not going to get better: everyone from the long-term victim of a serious illness to the schoolgirl convinced she will never understand algebra can be helped with the gentian remedy.

The remedy acts, then, on faith. It restores people's ability to believe in themselves and helps them to see that everything is possible if only they go on trying. Instead of sinking into a despondency that might well deepen if it is not treated, they can shake off their pessimistic thoughts and emerge into the light, able to accept and live with past upsets and go on to success and happiness.

CASE HISTORY: *Karen was in her twenties and had just undergone a minor gynaecological operation. Although the consultant had assured her of a full recovery, after a few days the discomfort she felt left her rather downhearted. She even began to think the operation had not been a success.*

As Karen was not in the genuine hopelessness and despair of the gorse state, gentian was prescribed along with wild rose, since this could give her more of the fighting spirit needed for a quick recovery.

Karen rapidly cheered up and, just as the specialist had predicted, the treatment was a complete success.

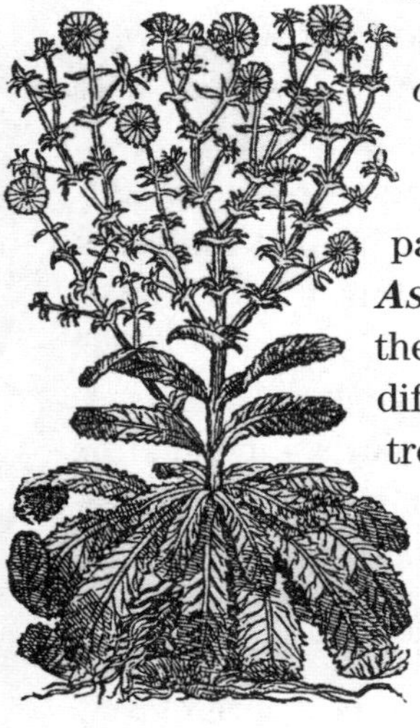

KEY SYMPTOMS: Discouragement caused by a particular setback or problem. Pessimism.

ASSOCIATED PROBLEMS: Tendency always to look on the black side. Doubt of one's abilities to overcome difficulties. Doubt of the wisdom of a course of treatment or action that is in fact working well. Generally, a lack of faith.

TREATMENT GOALS: Put one's reverses and disappointments into perspective. Encourage a positive outlook and faith in the future.

GORSE

(*Ulex europaeus*)

This remedy comes from an evergreen shrub also known as the common furze. As the name suggests, it is a common sight on dry, stony soil and open land generally. It is quite a dramatic-looking plant, about 2 metres high and covered with pointed glossy green spines and bright, golden yellow flowers that come and go from February until late autumn. The flowers are at their most abundant in late spring and early summer, which is when the remedy is prepared.

PREPARATION: By the sun method.

INDICATIONS: Gorse is called for when the failure of one or more treatments leads someone to abandon hope. More generally, it is the remedy for the hopelessness and despair people can feel when they have been given bad news of any kind about their health. And it is also used for those who have managed to convince themselves that there is nothing more to be done, even when there might actually be many cures that could be tried, any of which could have the positive result desired. The gorse state can be seen as a more serious version of the gentian state, and the differences between them as matters of degree rather than kind.

Like gentian people, the gorse type is something of a pessimist. However, even the most optimistic person can fall into a gorse state following an adverse diagnosis, particularly a life-threatening one. In this case especially, the feeling of despair and hopelessness can actually help to speed up the progress of the illness and make the worst come true all the quicker.

Sometimes the problems of gorse people do not have such a strong basis in fact and the diagnosis that has caused distress might be purely imaginary, for all that the despair is real. For example, some gorse types become convinced that they have some kind of inherited disease. This could be anything from acne to insanity; but whatever it is, the idea that it is 'in the family' leads to the feeling that nothing can be done about it.

It's hardly surprising that as a result of their despair gorse people attending their first flower remedy consultation often start off by saying that they don't believe the remedies can do anything to help them. There are numerous records of consultations with gorse people who say the only reason they have come at all is to please the sister, husband, wife, brother, parent, offspring or friend who suggested the idea.

Although it cannot work miracles, gorse renews hope and gives sufferers a new sense that life is still worth living and fighting for. It can also lend a certain detachment, so that sufferers are able to think and plan ahead unhindered by the despair commonly associated with chronic conditions.

If you are in any doubt about the seriousness of a physical condition it is always a good idea to recommend that the person concerned seeks qualified medical advice. The flower remedies can be given at the same time as any other course of medication or therapy, so there is no reason why orthodox medical intervention cannot be combined with the gentle, positive effects of the flower remedies.

The gorse state of hopelessness and despair should be distinguished carefully from the absolute, final despair of people in the sweet chestnut state. The latter is usually felt by someone who has fought long and bravely against great odds and will only submit to a final black despair when every possible avenue seems closed. The gorse state comes long before the end, and it is to allow the sufferer to begin the long fight that the gorse remedy is used.

CASE HISTORY: *Georgina had a good job and a contented home life, but for years she had been sleeping only three or four hours a night. Her mother had also had insomnia, and she was* *convinced that this was an inherited pattern about which nothing could be done. The feeling of hopelessness had intensified since she had been persuaded to try hypnotherapy, which had been unsuccessful.*

It might seem that the olive remedy was indicated, for the feelings of tiredness. However, Georgina's lack of hope and her feelings that she had inherited the problem suggested gorse instead. Although she was a difficult patient, who had to be persuaded to take the remedies regularly, she did find a gradual improvement. By the time she stopped taking the gorse, she was sleeping for six hours at a stretch most nights.

KEY SYMPTOMS: Hopelessness and despair, usually caused by an adverse medical diagnosis, accident, etc.
ASSOCIATED PROBLEMS: Unwillingness to try new treatments. Complaints of inherited conditions and chronic disease. Pale, sallow complexion.
TREATMENT GOALS: Give new heart so that the fight for health can be resumed. Encourage an objective, positive attitude. Often used to encourage patients to persevere with a course of treatment.

HEATHER

(*Calluna vulgaris*)

The variety of plant used to make the heather remedy is the true Scotch heather. This is a low shrubby plant with rough stems and lightly bristled branches. The tiny mauve flowers bloom, hundreds to a shrub, in late summer and early autumn. Heather is particularly associated with moorland, heaths and other exposed, dry areas.
PREPARATION: By the sun method.
INDICATIONS: People of the heather type are concerned only about themselves and their problems – and they talk incessantly about both. They are so intent on having an audience for

their woes that their persistence and unreasoning pursuit of listeners can make them appear mentally unbalanced. Certainly they don't seem to see or understand the reaction they provoke in other people, for when their hapless listeners try to break away, the heather person fails completely to get the hint and is likely to follow them down the road, back them into corners and even hold onto their sleeves or jacket lapels, talking all the while straight into their faces. No doubt this habit explains why heather types are known collectively as 'buttonholers'; others may know them as 'pub bores', or simply as self-centred, self-obsessed chatterboxes.

The fact that other people try to escape from them is one of the great ironies of the heather state, for their main anguish and fear is that they will be left alone and that no one will sympathize with them. To ensure that this will not happen they are very insistent, become weepy at times and exaggerate to make their interminable monologues more 'interesting'. Of course, the result is the opposite of the one intended.

The only way people can obtain genuine sympathy is if they are capable of sympathizing with other people's troubles as well as harping on their own – but heather people are terrible listeners and simply don't pay any attention to the replies or complaints of their victims. And if a word does get through, it simply serves as the trigger for another set of reminiscences and instances that soon lose all contact with the original thread.

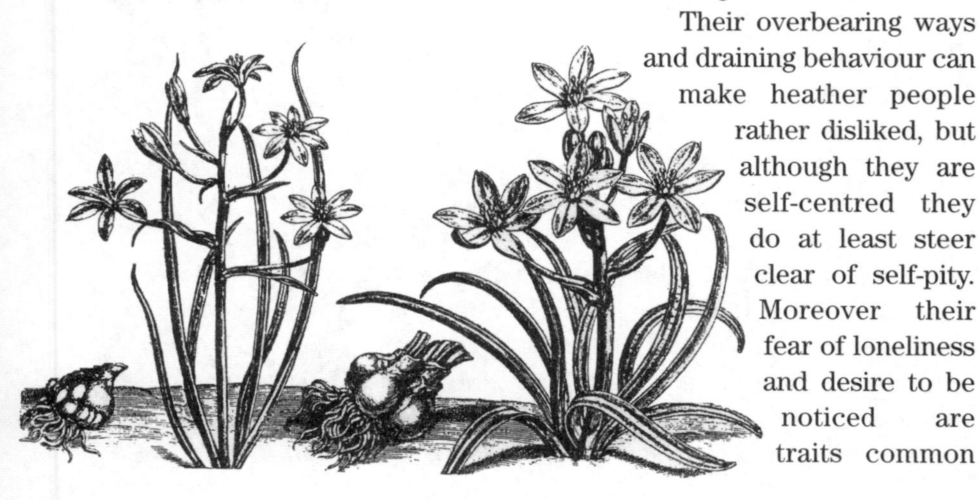

Their overbearing ways and draining behaviour can make heather people rather disliked, but although they are self-centred they do at least steer clear of self-pity. Moreover their fear of loneliness and desire to be noticed are traits common

to most of humanity: the fact that these characteristics are so pronounced and persistent in heather people is only a sign that they need help. Besides, almost anyone can fall into a temporary heather state when a worry or preoccupation leads us to drone on and on to an uninterested audience. Just like the longer-term sufferers, we too can lose the ability to see the wider picture by overconcentrating on our own place in the scheme of things.

Heather is the remedy for all these conditions. It helps turn self-obsessed talkers into people who can see themselves as others do, and then choose to be different. Having known what it is like to need to talk when no one wants to listen, reformed heather types can make in turn excellent, sympathetic listeners and counsellors.

CASE HISTORY: *Noreen had always been a chatterbox. When her dog died her neighbours offered their sympathy, but instead of recovering from her loss Noreen continued to talk about it in great detail. She repeatedly recounted the everyday problems she was having, frequently bursting into tears. At first her neighbours listened sympathetically, but then they began to avoid her. She could see this happening and it caused her much pain.*

To deal with her self-obsession and inability to look beyond her troubles to those of other people, Noreen was given heather. Star of Bethlehem was added because she had not come to terms with her pet's death. There was a gradual improvement, and a milestone was reached when a flood left some of her neighbours temporarily homeless. In helping them she rediscovered the ability to listen to others, and as a result found that they were more willing to listen to her.

KEY SYMPTOMS: Self-obsession. Self-centredness. Aggressively talkative.
ASSOCIATED PROBLEMS: Fear of being alone. Can be shunned by friends and acquaintances. Exaggeration and weepiness. Hypochondria.
TREATMENT GOALS: Turn from a talker to a listener. Give strength to help others and cope with one's own concerns.

HOLLY

(*Ilex aquifolium*)

The evergreen holly is of course normally associated with Christmas, and is a familiar sight with its dark green branches, prickly leaves and bright red berries. The white flowers are perhaps less well known, partly because they appear in early summer when holly doesn't stand out so much, but also because they are very small and grow tucked up close to the leaves' axils.
PREPARATION: By the boiling method.
INDICATIONS: Holly is the remedy indicated for some of the most negative emotional states that people can suffer from: hatred, envy, jealousy, overpowering suspicion and aggression. Because these are all very powerful and destructive states, holly is in some ways the most important of all the remedies: without it many people can be hurt, not just the immediate sufferer.

In direct contrast to those other resentful types, the willow people, the negative feelings experienced in the holly state are not sulky so much as fiery. Holly people may or may not show their emotions outwardly, but when they do they are prone to outbursts of anger during which they rant and rave and can become physically aggressive.

Although it can sometimes be difficult to sympathize with holly types, it's important to remember that the unattractive feelings they manifest are a form of disease. Even though they appear to be suffering for no good reason, and you may feel more sympathy for the innocent people on whom they fix their anger, nevertheless their suffering is very real. Put simply, it comes from an absence of love that makes life seem empty and the personality feel cheated and alone. The symptoms can all be seen as opposites of the generous emotion of love: envy and jealousy where love would be glad at another's happiness; hatred and the desire to do harm replacing affection and the desire to help; and suspicion instead of trust. That other symptom sometimes found in people suffering from the holly state – greed – is the personality's way of trying to compensate for the love and affection of which it is starved. It's as if the individual is trying to cram his or her life with material things so as to fill an emotional emptiness.

The holly remedy drives out jealousy, hatred and suspicion, love's dark shadows, and replaces them with the genuine article. At the same time it opens up the blocked channels of communication between the individual and others, so that the angry person is able to share once more and take delight in other people's fulfilment and success.

Case history: *Cora was an only child, calm and healthy, until she was two years old, when her mother gave birth to twins. This came as a terrible shock. Cora suddenly came down with a succession of illnesses, including 'flu, diarrhoea and asthma attacks. When she wasn't ill, she would fly into dreadful tempers when she would lash out at her baby sisters.*

This jealousy and anger indicated the holly remedy. Although the other illnesses quickly cleared up and Cora began to accept the twins, the asthma continued. Star of Bethlehem was added for the shock she had experienced when her sisters were born; for although this was now some time in the past it was felt that she had not got over it.

Within a few weeks the asthma had eased. Soon Cora was attending a nursery school, where she was able to mix with the other children without jealousy or temper.

Remember that the remedies are preserved in brandy, and when giving them to children make sure that you dilute them as described in chapter 3. Undiluted flower remedies from prepared stock bottles should only be used in an emergency, and then a few drops only should be given on the tongue.

KEY SYMPTOMS: Intense hatred. Spiteful aggression. Envy and jealousy.
ASSOCIATED PROBLEMS: Outbursts of temper. Suspicion of other people's actions and motives.
TREATMENT GOALS: Restore harmony and ability to share. Restore faith in and love for others.

HONEYSUCKLE

(*Lonicera caprifolium*)

This is a climbing plant with a tough, woody stem. The more common variety of honeysuckle (*Lonicera periclymenum*) has yellow flowers and can easily be confused with *Lonicera caprifolium*, whose flowers turn yellow following pollination. Before this, however, they are a dark pink on the outside with a delicate, white inner part. Identification of the correct *Lonicera caprifolium* is made even more difficult by the fact that there are many varieties of cultivated honeysuckle, some of which have now seeded in the wild.
PREPARATION: Although honeysuckle blooms in the hottest part of the year – in June and July – the remedy is prepared using the boiling method.

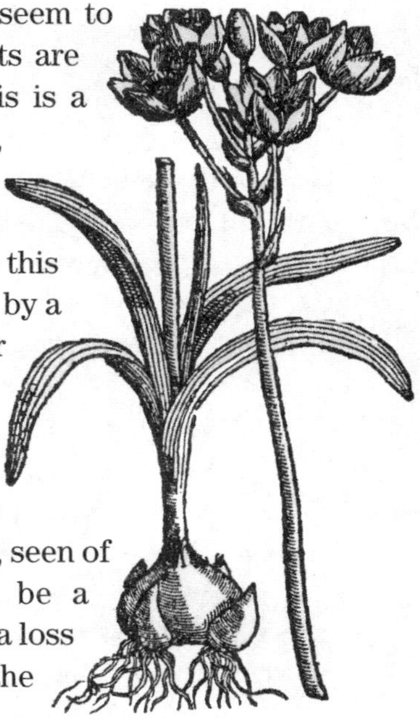

Indications: Honeysuckle is for people who seem to miss out on the present because their thoughts are always in the past. As you might imagine, this is a condition usually associated with older people, who as they get on in years find it easier and easier to lose themselves in nostalgic recollections of their younger days. Sometimes this desire to look back instead of forward is driven by a fear of the present and the future. With older people this is often the case when the sufferer is living alone: widows and widowers, for instance, can fall into a state of mind in which it seems as if there is little to look forward to except a gradual decline, in which case the past, seen of course through rose-tinted spectacles, can be a convenient escape. In any case, there is always a loss of interest in the present that can leave the sufferer appearing vague and absent-minded.

The honeysuckle state is not confined to older people, however; it can just as easily overwhelm much younger ones. Children starting a new school, for example, often think back to their own 'golden age', even if it is only days or weeks in the past. If they have to live at the school as well, the feelings can be even stronger and be mixed up with homesickness. Although the state might usually be more short-lived in the young than it is in the old, the feeling that things will never be as good as they once were can be equally strong for both groups.

So far we have assumed that the memories controlling the honeysuckle person's present are happy ones, but this is far from always being the case. At times they can be unpleasant – such as regrets and thoughts about missed opportunities and failed wishes – or even downright frightening. The soldier who dreams every night of the battle in which he was wounded could benefit from honeysuckle to help him keep his thoughts on the present, perhaps with rock rose for the extreme terror he feels or star of Bethlehem for the unresolved shock the noise and panic of the battlefield caused him.

Anyone can suffer from the honeysuckle state during moments of boredom or frustration. At times like these it can be a pleasant escape, and in small doses there is little harm in dreaming of the past. But if there is any danger that the state will stop the person's progress in the present, the remedy can usefully be given to allow the mind to leave the past and move on. The memories will not be erased, and the lessons to be learnt from past experiences will not be forgotten, but the person's real vital interest will be focused on the present where it can do most good and achieve more happiness.

Case history: *Dawn had been threatened by a gang of older girls when she was ten years old. They chased her through a park, and when they caught her they stole her pocket money and new watch. Thirty years later, the incident was still much in her mind and she still grew nervous whenever there were large groups of children around.*

Honeysuckle was given to help Dawn move away from her unhappy memories, along with star of Bethlehem for the shock she had experienced. Her fear left her, and most importantly she was able to start to enjoy the company of her teenage daughters and their friends.

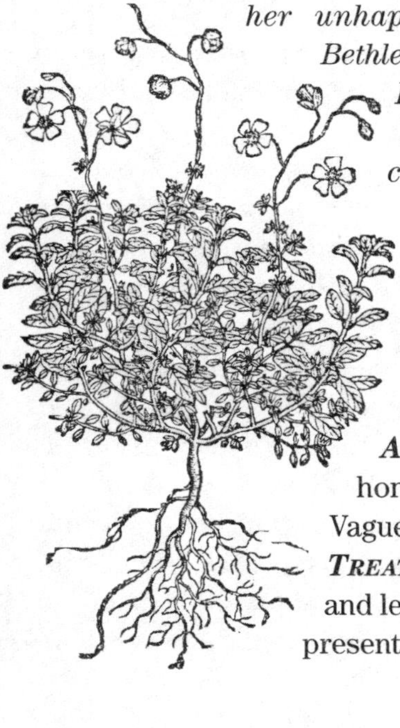

Key symptoms: Living in the past. Ignoring or fleeing from the present and taking refuge or becoming trapped in memories.

Associated problems: Nostalgia and homesickness. Regrets. Inability to let go. Vagueness.

Treatment goals: Allow the person to value and learn from the past while living in and for the present.

HORNBEAM

(*Carpinus betulus*)

The hornbeam tree looks a little like a smaller version of the beech tree and has a similar silver-grey bark. Both male and female flowers are found on the same tree, appearing in April and May. The males are green-brown catkins, about 2-5 centimetres long, which hang down from the branch. The females grow upright in pairs and only begin to droop when the fruit has started to form.

Preparation: By the boiling method.

Indications: The hornbeam state is characterized by a feeling of weariness and fatigue when faced with work that needs doing or duties that have to be fulfilled. People who are diagnosed as being in this state do not usually have any trouble getting down to work, but then find that they are not sure about their strength and their ability to cope. Theirs is a tiredness more of the mind than the body, caused by the thought of work rather than the work itself. Because it feels so vague and so often relates to everyday tasks, it is frequently referred to as the 'Monday morning feeling'.

People in this state may obtain no refreshment however long they rest, and often actually feel worse after a night's sleep. If they delay starting to tackle a task, their strength isn't stored up anew, as it would be if the cause were physical; rather, they feel weaker and less able to cope the longer they go without beginning work. Indeed, if only people in this state could set about the task before them they would find that their normal enthusiasm and energy soon return. But the lethargy and lack of interest caused by the hornbeam state prevent them from taking this positive step.

In all these cases, the remedy works to restore people's confidence in their own strength. Crucially, it also gives them the push they need to pick up their burdens again and continue in an optimistic and positive frame of mind, even where the tasks in hand may seem genuinely too much for one person to deal with. Where the tiredness has been exacerbated by the person's being in a rut at work, this increase in

optimism and renewed ability to take things on can actually help him or her to break out of the routine.

Hornbeam can also help those who recover from an illness only to find that the thought of resuming their normal lives makes them feel weak and lethargic. If the same people are left physically weakened after convalescing, olive is the indicated remedy. Often the two are combined if there are elements of both states.

CASE HISTORY: *Jerry and his wife Roberta had been saving for years to build an extension to their house and had spent countless enjoyable evenings deciding exactly what they wanted. But when they obtained planning permission and were all ready to go, Jerry suddenly lost all enthusiasm. He put off going to see the builders and found hundreds of reasons to delay starting the work.*

Hornbeam was given to deal with Jerry's procrastination and lethargic state. He was able to get the project going again, and once things were moving his enthusiasm returned undiminished.

KEY SYMPTOMS: Fatigue at the thought of completing a task or doing a job. The Monday morning feeling.
ASSOCIATED PROBLEMS: Feelings of being in a rut. Procrastination.
TREATMENT GOALS: Restore strength and optimism. Allow the sufferer to resume positive action.

IMPATIENS

(*Impatiens glandulifera*)

Impatiens is an annual that grows up to 2 metres high and is especially fond of damp conditions. The green or crimson stems are ribbed and semi-opaque, the alternate leaves are green with a crimson rib, and the flowers, which grow at the top of the plant from July to September and have a pronounced lower lip, range from a pale mauve to a dark crimson-mauve.

Preparation: By the sun method, using only the pale mauve flowers.

Indications: The name of the impatiens remedy is a good clue to the type of person who can benefit from its use. People of this kind are quick-witted and fast-moving, very competent and able, finding it easy to grasp new ideas and concepts as soon as they are encountered. This means they can find it hard to have to wait for their slower colleagues to catch up. Consequently they become very impatient, and may finish other people's sentences, thoughts or work for them in the effort to keep things moving along, even if this means doing tasks officially reserved for a subordinate. Thus impatiens people tend not to make good managers, and given the chance they usually prefer to forego leadership and keep their independence so that they can work alone and at their own pace. If this is impossible they occasionally try, in their quick and impatient way, to find ways to help other people work faster, and may even feel a moral obligation to do so. To them, there seems something inherently wrong and wasteful in not going as fast as possible.

If things move too slowly for impatiens people, they can easily become frustrated and irritable. They may even lose their tempers all of a sudden. Fortunately, however quick they are to get angry they are just as quick to calm down again, and they do not generally bear grudges for long.

Nervous and overhasty in everything they do, impatiens types can feel as if their minds are always leaping way ahead of their bodies. Consequently they can appear clumsy at times, and by rushing in where others fear to tread they can be very accident-prone. This is particularly the case when they are suffering one of their frequent bouts of irritation, for then they tend to vent their frustrations by slamming doors and banging things about, often catching their own fingers in the process. And when they are laid up as the result of a particularly severe mishap, or are ill for any other reason, they can become very anxious at the time it is taking them to get well again, which of course is counterproductive.

There are definite physical signs to watch out for that help mark out the impatiens person. Quick, nervous movements are typical, especially tapping feet and drumming fingers that indicate a desire to get away from a long conversation. So are twitches of all kinds and constant fidgeting – impatiens people find it hard to keep still for long. Indigestion caused by tension and rushed meals is also common, as are nervous rashes.

The remedy helps impatiens types to become more relaxed and more prepared to help others see and play out their roles in wider society. As their irritability fades, they discover new depths of patience and tolerance. In short, the remedy adds an active heart to their already active intellects, to produce a more rounded and well-balanced personality.

CASE HISTORY: *Steven had been suffering from various minor illnesses: colds, sinus trouble, sore throats and so on. Each time he had to take time off work he worried a great deal, as he did not think his colleagues could meet the tight deadlines his job demanded.*

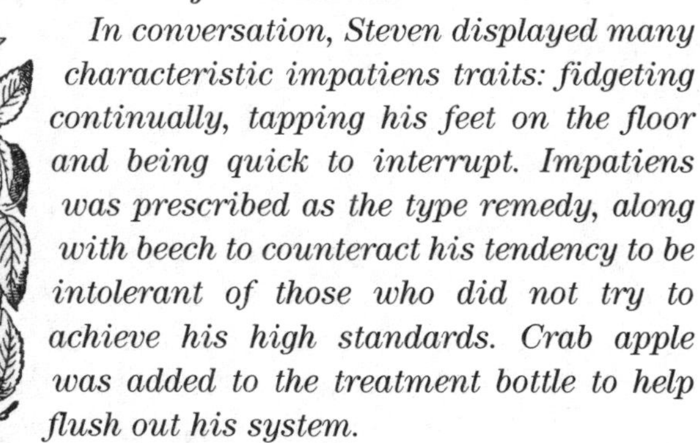

In conversation, Steven displayed many characteristic impatiens traits: fidgeting continually, tapping his feet on the floor and being quick to interrupt. Impatiens was prescribed as the type remedy, along with beech to counteract his tendency to be intolerant of those who did not try to achieve his high standards. Crab apple was added to the treatment bottle to help flush out his system.

Over a year later, Steven reported that he had only had two very minor colds since starting the remedies.

KEY SYMPTOMS: Impatience and irritability. Desire to do everything quickly.

ASSOCIATED PROBLEMS: Tension, nervousness, twitches and inability to sit still. Indigestion.

TREATMENT GOALS: Increase empathy with others and patience with people and situations.

LARCH

(Larix decidua)

This tall, straight tree grows up to 30 metres high. It flowers in April, when the new leaves have just started to show as bristly tufts along the length of the smaller branches and twigs. Both male and female flowers appear on the same tree, growing interspersed with new leaves. The female flowers are squat, rounded catkins up to 2.5 centimetres long and are easy to spot as they are bright red. The somewhat smaller male flowers are much the same shape, but with yellow stamens supported by scales.

PREPARATION: By the boiling method.

INDICATIONS: While cerato people have no confidence in the decisions they take, but try things and hope for good results, larch people are inclined not to attempt anything, so convinced are they that they are bound to fail. Theirs is the definitive inferiority complex, for they are sure in their own minds that they are not as good as other people and that they cannot do as well as others. They can always come up with a hundred good reasons not to try something, but none in favour of a bold attempt. What they suffer from, then, is a disastrous and life-sapping lack of confidence.

Some larch types may find a perverse comfort in standing to one side. They believe they are behaving sensibly in avoiding useless effort. They can also be warm in their admiration of more dynamic people, as if to point up the good judgement that they possess and so implicitly underline the sense in not trying such things themselves. At least they

are saving wasted effort, they say, but they are wrong to do so: if they once accept the risk of failure they usually find that they are just as capable as other people and that their plans and ambitions are just as likely to be realized as anyone else's. Indeed, in many cases the humble larch types turn out to be more talented than the people they praise.

If some larch people are sanguine about their imagined inadequacy, others are far less so, and their feelings of uselessness can lead to a great deal of unhappiness and despondency. In any case, all larch people risk living frustrated and unnecessarily limited lives, for we all have only a certain number of opportunities in life and larch people are capable of letting them all slip by if they are not given encouragement. This is a tragic waste, so whether or not the people being treated are content or not to stand always in the background the remedy can do a great deal of good simply by encouraging them to plunge into life in a more wholehearted way. There is no guarantee they will be successful, but there is much to be gained, for sufferers are able to meet triumph and disaster with equanimity, take risks and not feel ashamed of the occasional failure.

Anyone can be in a temporary larch state, and the remedy can be used to tackle any new situations or problems in general which give rise to a lack of confidence. To give just one example, larch can be helpful if you are about to take an exam and have been thinking that you may as well not turn up, since you are bound to fail. Larch gives you the confidence to have a go and, if you do fail, the confidence to ride out your disappointment and try again.

CASE HISTORY: *Julie worked for a small import/export company. When her supervisor suddenly left, she was immediately promoted. The responsibilities of her new job threw Julie into something approaching panic*

Her complete lack of confidence in her abilities indicated the need for larch. Julie took this remedy, with gentian added periodically when she became discouraged, throughout her first five months in the job. The panic disappeared almost at once, and gradually her confidence in her own abilities increased so that by the end of the period she was planning what additional skills and training she would need to take on even more responsibilities.

KEY SYMPTOMS: Lack of self-confidence. Feelings of inferiority. Fearful of trying to succeed.
ASSOCIATED PROBLEMS: Passivity and lack of will-power.
TREATMENT GOALS: Instil confidence in abilities. Increase courage and will-power. Remove fear of failure.

MIMULUS

(*Mimulus guttatus*)

The mimulus is a water-loving perennial, growing up to 30 centimetres high along the sides of streams, rivers and other wet places. The large, single flowers are a rich yellow, with tiny red spots under the opening to the corolla. They appear in high summer, from June to August.
PREPARATION: By the sun method.
INDICATIONS: Mimulus is the remedy for the fear of known things, that is to say fear which has a known cause that the person suffering the fear is able to name. Under this heading we find the fear of redundancy, fear of illness and infirmity, fear of going to the dentist or climbing a high ladder, and the anxiety some people feel when they have to stand up to give a speech, for all are rational, 'normal' fears. The child scared of

going to school for the first time is in a mimulus state, as is the pensioner who is frightened of being mugged.

Other mimulus fears shade into the aspen state, for they may have an irrational, inexplicable side. For example, fear of the dark is a fear of a known thing, but it often has another, causeless side when the sufferer imagines all kind of vague, nameless horrors. Even people afraid of pigeons, spiders or mice – on the face of it typical mimulus fears – can skirt the borderline between a known and an unknown fear when these phobias are found together with a kind of vague, inexplicable horror, even when the apparent cause is not physically present. As these states can be difficult to separate, mimulus and aspen are sometimes given in tandem when both elements seem to be present.

At the extreme of fear, when feelings of pure terror and panic arise that are completely uncontrollable, the indicated remedy is rock rose. By seeing these three remedies as a spectrum, with aspen on the supernatural side and rock rose on the side of pure terror, mimulus is placed in the middle as the most mundane, everyday and normal fear. It is not surprising then that this remedy is the most prescribed of the three.

Mimulus types are those who seem to live in a state of reasonable fear most of the time. They tend to be nervous and shy, and under pressure may stammer, blush or talk far too fast in the attempt to hide their fear. They tend to avoid social gatherings and any occasions where they would be obliged to put themselves forward: the mimulus type obliged to speak at a wedding is a pitiful sight. Because they are so shy, any phobias and other more serious fears they have are often kept to themselves, for the mimulus person does not open up to others lightly.

The remedy is given in all such cases to remove the fear and give sufferers a quiet courage that can help them to face life's problems with a lighter and more confident heart. Once the fear is removed they can find a renewed pleasure in life; in some cases, where the fear has been present since childhood, the relief can almost be equivalent to a second birth. In more everyday cases, when a temporary fear of some thing or condition is to be overcome, the remedy gives fast relief and quickly brings runaway emotions under control.

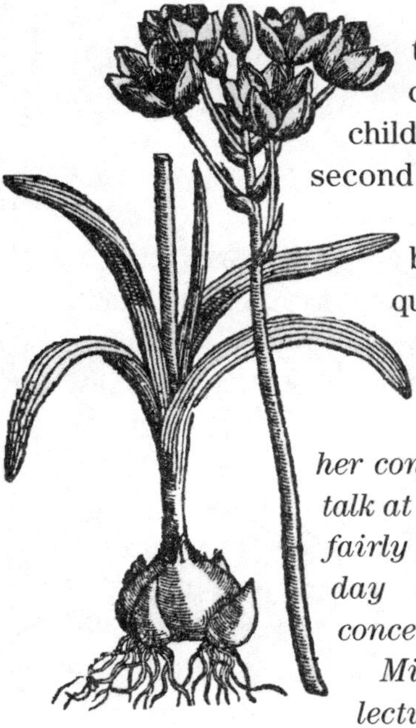

Case history: *Jane was in her forties, outwardly a self-confident extrovert, in a fairly senior administrative position. But her confidence fled when she was asked to give a talk at a conference. Although she knew the subject fairly well, her fear increased as the appointed day approached and she was unable to concentrate on her preparation.*

Mimulus was given during the week before the lecture, along with white chestnut for the obsessive worry that was interfering with Jane's preparation. Her nerves didn't entirely disappear, but she calmed down enough for her natural self-confidence to begin to shine through. She prepared her talk and, fortified by a quick sip of mimulus before the speech began, made a successful debut as a public speaker.

Key symptoms: Fear of specific, everyday things and situations. Any fear where a cause can be named.
Associated problems: Shyness, timidity, blushing and stammering.
Treatment goals: Give courage to face and overcome fear. Allow the person to grow and move beyond the limits set by anxieties and phobias. Restore rationality.

MUSTARD

(*Sinapis arvensis*)

The wild mustard grows up to 60 centimetres high along roadsides and in fields. It is an annual, with clusters of yellow flowers appearing at the end of the upright, bristly stems from May to July. The leaves are rough and crinkled, growing straight from the stem towards the top of the plant and attached to short stalks at the bottom.

Preparation: Unusually for a remedy prepared from flower heads, the boiling method is used for mustard.

Indications: Just as aspen is the remedy for a causeless fear, so mustard is indicated whenever there is depression without just cause. This is the black depression that seems to descend out of nowhere, taking away all joy in life and making its victims feel as if there is no point to anything any more. It comes suddenly and can be as severe as it is sudden, but when asked why they feel so down people in this state can only shrug their shoulders. Indeed, they will often come up with any number of reasons why they should be happy – good marriages, rewarding careers, healthy children and so on – and will be totally at a loss as to why they should feel this way.

In truth there is no logical explanation for the mustard state and it is pointless to look for one. The depression has no connection with the person's everyday life or innermost thoughts: it can only be thought of as an unwelcome barrier between a healthy joy in living and the sufferer. And it goes as it comes, suddenly and inexplicably.

This is a condition that is often found in teenagers; for example, where the emotions associated with reaching maturity overbalance one way or another, with wild hilarity at one moment and hopelessness the next, and no sufficient reason for either. But people of all ages can fall into the same condition, and for all of them mustard is the remedy

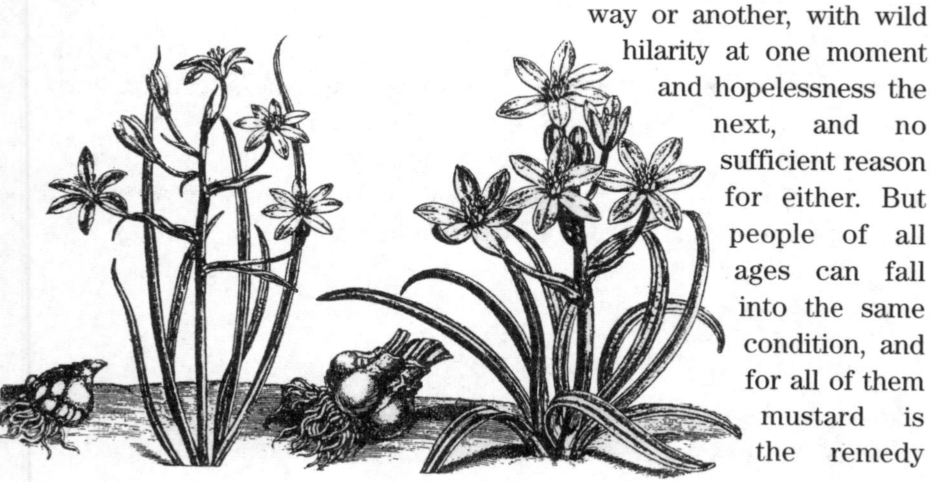

that can help dispel the black clouds sooner, bringing these people back to emotional equilibrium.

For people who suffer from such states frequently, the remedy is given as part of a treatment bottle over a period of weeks or months, building up the person's inner strength and stability so that the condition will be less likely to recur. Many people who have suffered from inexplicable depressions for years have been helped back to a normal and happy existence by the bright yellow flowers of the mustard.

CASE HISTORY: *Victoria saw us on behalf of her fifteen-year-old son Jake. He was a bright boy and doing well at school, but every two or three months would fall into a deep depression. It only lasted a few days, during which he refused to leave his room except for meals. When the depression had lifted he couldn't give any reason for it except that the world seemed black and there seemed no reason to do anything.*

Victoria was advised to give Jake mustard. Six months later she reported that there had been only one further bout of depression, lasting for less than twenty-four hours.

KEY SYMPTOMS: Black depression with no apparent cause. Vague gloom and melancholia.
ASSOCIATED PROBLEMS: Thoughts all turned inwards. Finds no joy in normal pleasures.
TREATMENT GOALS: Restore emotional equilibrium. Attain serenity and stability with no fear of future attacks. Regain joy in living.

OAK

(*Quercus robur*)

The common oak is a familiar sight, with its sculpted leaves, thick trunk and, in the autumn, acorns. It was once thought to have magical powers and was strongly associated with the ancient druids.

The oak is a deciduous tree, with the flowers and leaves arriving together in April or May. Both male and female catkins grow on the same tree, with the yellow-green males being the easiest to spot, as they droop down in loose clusters; the females are hidden among the leaves in groups of three or four, each consisting of three bright crimson styles in a calyx in the form of a cup. This calyx later forms the acorn's cap.

Preparation: By the sun method, using the female flowers alone.

Indications: Like the tree, oak people are stout-hearted and strong. They are the types who will struggle on against adversity and illness without losing hope. With spiritual strength even greater that their undoubted physical strength, they give freely of their time and energies, and will fight and work as hard for the people who rely on them as they do for themselves. Consequently they often find themselves at the centre of a network of people who are in trouble or need help, for those less able know they will always find succour and assistance from the oak type.

All of these characteristics are of course entirely good and noble, and there is no question of the remedy somehow 'curing' oak people of their strength and reliability, or of their desire to give service to other people. The problems that the remedy can help with come not so much from the good spiritual qualities already mentioned, as from their inevitable results on the mind and body, as the oak type has a definite tendency to overwork and to try to hide tiredness so as not to let other people down. This tenacity sometimes slides into sheer obstinacy, so that these people can reject the good advice of loved ones who ask them to slow down or simply take a rest every so often. Their great strength means that they can get away with this for a long time, but eventually there will come a crash, and the longer it is delayed the more severe it is likely to be. They can even get to the point of suffering from nervous breakdowns and physical exhaustion. When they are ill they can become very despondent and unhappy with what

they are likely to see as their own weakness, and especially upset if they feel they are disappointing people who are relying on them.

Whenever oak people get near this state of physical, mental or emotional breakdown, the remedy is there to help. It restores their natural strength and positive outlook so that they are able to resume work once more. And they do so with a renewed sense of the importance of their efforts and with their innate patience and common sense enhanced. This means that they can stand even greater stresses and strains than they did before – and at the same time they understand the need for occasional rest and relaxation.

CASE HISTORY: *Claire was a health visitor in a poor part of London who worked with many families in very difficult circumstances. She had been suffering from headaches, mouth ulcers and a throbbing wisdom tooth. Her dentist could find nothing wrong.*

Oak was the only remedy given, since Claire's determination to carry on despite her problems was characteristic of this type. She soon reported feeling stronger and less tired, and the headaches cleared up. But the ulcers and toothache were still there and she was becoming rather despondent about them. Gentian was added to counteract this feeling and it seemed to do the trick. Free of her ailments, Claire returned to work with renewed enthusiasm.

KEY SYMPTOMS: Struggling on through great adversity. Never giving up. Bravery and hope against all odds.
ASSOCIATED PROBLEMS: Overwork and tiredness, usually hidden. Obstinacy. Possible eventual breakdown if not helped.
TREATMENT GOALS: Restore high natural levels of strength and courage.

OLIVE

(*Olea europoea*)

The olive tree is an evergreen that grows up to 12 metres high and is common in the warmer parts of Europe. It is one of the few remedy plants that is not native to Britain. The leaves are long and thick, pale green, and glossy. The flowers, which appear in clusters of twenty or thirty, are very small and white. The exact month of the year in which they appear varies from country to country, but it is always in spring.

PREPARATION: By the sun method.

INDICATIONS: Olive is the remedy for complete exhaustion. Whenever someone has suffered for a long time or has worked too much so that strength has failed and vitality has been sapped, this is the indicated remedy to restore the lost energy. Similarly it is called for in cases where a *long illness or protracted convalescence has left the person feeling weak and unable to go on making the effort to get well.

Like all the flower remedies, olive can be used in conjunction with any other course of treatment or therapy. This makes it an ideal supplement to help restore the vigour and strength of anyone exhausted by a long illness or its after-effects.

The olive state can be either mental or physical, or a mixture of the two. The physical condition is characterized by a great fatigue that makes even the smallest task seem too much to bear. Every movement becomes an effort; even if sufficient strength is found to try to do something, sufferers tire very quickly because they have such poor reserves of strength. Mentally, people in the olive state are unable to get any enjoyment out of activities that they once liked. Everything seems to be hard work, and they cannot find the enthusiasm they once had for work or social activities; instead they sink into a kind of lethargy. To use a more popular phrase, their get-up-and-go gets up and goes.

Sometimes the hornbeam state and the olive state can be difficult to tell apart. The key is that the hornbeam state is entirely or mainly in the mind: it is the thought of the day ahead that makes the person feel tired. In contrast, the olive state always comes after a period of genuine effort, whether mental, physical or emotional, so that there is a definite cause for the tiredness. For instance, tiredness due to lack of sleep or overwork can be helped with olive, although one should always look for the underlying causes of the lack of sleep or overwork as other remedies might also be indicated. As examples, oak might be given if the overwork was due to the person's obstinately taking on too much, or white chestnut if perpetual worry is causing insomnia. As these examples suggest, olive is often given as a 'helper' remedy to back up the type remedy and its treatment of the root cause.

The main action of the olive remedy is to restore the person's strength and vitality – but just as importantly it helps restore mental balance. Many people who frequently fall into the olive state are living unbalanced lives where poor diet, too many late nights or the attempt to fit too much into each day is leaving them exhausted. This is the imbalance the remedy can address, allowing the person treated to live a stable and full life, unworried by excessive tiredness.

CASE HISTORY: *After injuring his legs very badly in a car crash, Gerald had to undergo a long, gruelling course of physiotherapy. His progress was hampered by complete exhaustion - which in the physiotherapist's opinion was partly mental and emotional (caused by the upheavals in his life since the accident) and partly physical (caused by the effort required to do the exercises).*

Both olive and hornbeam were given throughout the physiotherapy and Gerald was able to progress much faster than he might otherwise have done.

KEY SYMPTOMS: Exhaustion following effort of some kind. Mental and physical tiredness.
ASSOCIATED PROBLEMS: Loss of interest in life, hobbies, work, etc. Unbalanced approach to life caused by burning the candle at both ends.
TREATMENT GOALS: Restore strength and vitality. Help restore balance in those who live unbalanced, exhausting lives.

PINE

(*Pinus sylvestris*)

The tree used for this remedy is the Scots pine, an evergreen conifer growing about 24 metres high, with a straight purple-grey to red-brown trunk and short, spreading branches. The leaves are needles growing in thick, bushy tufts at the end of scaly twigs, with resinous buds in the middle of each tuft. The small male flowers are yellow and grow in clusters; the female cones are green at first, then turn red-brown as they ripen.
PREPARATION: By the boiling method, using a mixture of male and female flowers when they are full of pollen.
INDICATIONS: Pine is the remedy for people who take all the blame for things going wrong, whether or not they are really responsible. They are always apologizing for everything, even when they seem to have done

absolutely nothing wrong. Even when they are in the right, for example when asking an inconsiderate companion to stop playing loud music late at night, or asking a superior for time off work to attend a doctor's appointment, they always start by saying how sorry they are.

People of this type often feel remorse over some past event, and it is as if all the subsequent guilt they feel stems from this one occasion. Sometimes the past event was something that they are right to feel sorry for – an unkindness or wicked action – but instead of atoning for the act and moving on they have become trapped by their remorse. In other instances the past act was something that no sensible person would blame them for. This is the case, for example, with those children who blame themselves for their parents' divorce.

Sometimes pine people subconsciously try to punish themselves for their guilt by getting themselves into situations where they will be victimized. They might choose an unsuitable or even violent partner, or gamble wildly at cards or on the horses with the unconscious desire to lose. They also set themselves impossibly high ideals and moral standards, and the consequent disappointment they feel when they fail to meet them provides another excuse for self-punishment. And it is typical of pine people that when others fail to meet these same standards, the blame is once more somehow shouldered by the pine: the real guilty ones are absolved.

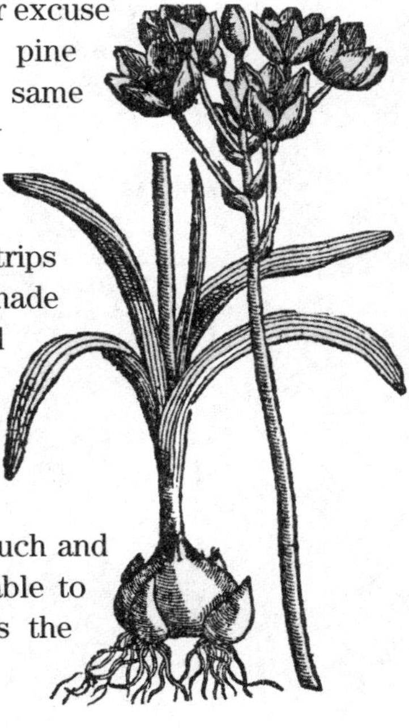

The guilt felt by pine people eventually strips life of all pleasure. Everything they do is made joyless by their continual self-reproach and they can end up believing themselves to be completely worthless. Even their efforts to do good are no help to them, because they are never content with the things they have done. This may lead them to take on too much and when (as inevitably happens) they are unable to cope with everything, this only reinforces the vicious circle of guilt and blame.

The remedy is taken to break this cycle of recrimination. Instead of taking the blame for everything, sufferers are able to judge where they did well and where they did ill, and in the latter case take action to remedy the ill and then move on. Real responsibility and humility are therefore achieved, in that even negative actions in the past can be the occasion of positive growth in the present.

CASE HISTORY: *Philip had been suffering from sciatica for months. He seemed to see it as a punishment for his past, when he had been unfaithful to his wife and experimented with drugs. At times he drank to try to deaden the pain, and when he drank too much he sometimes lost control of himself and lashed out at his wife and children. He was terrified that they would leave him, although he said that it would be his own fault if they did.*

Remember that the stock bottles of flower remedies are preserved in brandy. Never give them to anyone you think might be an alcoholic without explaining this to them first. In any case, they should always be diluted as explained in chapter 3, and never given neat.
The psychological effects on a recovering alcoholic of drinking even a small amount of alcohol can be very great. Seek medical advice if you are in doubt about whether to give remedies in this situation.

Pine was chosen as the type remedy for this self-destructive behaviour and guilt. Cherry plum was added to help Philip control his moods, and gorse since he was in despair at his own failings, and extremely pessimistic about any improvement.

There was no overnight change, but Philip persevered with the remedies and eventually joined his local branch of Alcoholics Anonymous. Once he had stopped drinking, progress was much quicker.

KEY SYMPTOMS: Self-reproach and guilt, often groundless. Guilt assumed for other people's faults.
ASSOCIATED PROBLEMS: High ideals set for self but not for others. Self-punishing or self-destructive behaviour; for example drinking, gambling, masochism.
TREATMENT GOALS: Enable sufferers to learn from and rectify past mistakes, then move on. Encourage positive responsibility and good judgement.

RED CHESTNUT

(*Aesculus carnea*)

This tree is of the same family as the horse chestnut, but smaller and more delicate. It has the same compound leaves, with their characteristic droopy look when they first appear in spring. Also like its larger cousin, the red chestnut has paired buds along its twigs, with a single large bud at the tip, all of them covered in resin. The buds bloom in May or June, producing large and very erect clusters of coral-coloured flowers.

PREPARATION: By the boiling method.
INDICATIONS: Red chestnut is the indicated remedy for a particular form of anxiety: fear that something bad will happen to someone else. Sometimes there is no basis at all for this fear, since the person being worried about is entirely well and able to look after him or herself. This is the fear felt by the child who loses one parent and fears that something will happen to the other one. It is also seen in parents

who are overconcerned for their grown-up son or daughter and become sick with worry if he or she comes home from work later than usual.

At other times there may be some basis for the fear, but the fear itself is extreme and the reaction exaggerated. Parents often fall into this state when their children are ill with 'flu or some other insignificant illness. Their love for their children magnifies minor problems into life-threatening conditions. Parents also show to a marked degree a typical red chestnut characteristic: their fear for themselves practically disappears. A mother worried about her five-year-old's rash will forget her own health or personal problems entirely.

It can be hard to persuade people in the red chestnut state that their condition is anything other than a selfless and noble quality, especially since they are not at all possessive or self-serving in their fussing, as for example chicory people are. Moreover, they often don't realize that anyone has noticed their worrying, and so see theirs as a purely personal problem that doesn't hurt anyone else.

This is not the case, however, for the results of red chestnut concern are entirely negative. On a minor level, their constant worrying can become very tiresome for the people they worry about, sapping their energy and trying their patience. But there is a more serious problem too.

Whether or not there is any basis to the fear, the overconcern shown by people in the red chestnut state has a potentially serious effect on those being worried about. Fear is contagious, and people who might otherwise not be scared of the situation they are in will become so because of the obvious anxiety shown about them and their condition. Where there is a real cause for concern, for example an injury or a serious illness, communicating fear and panic to the patient is obviously not a good idea.

This, then, is one of those remedies that is good not only for the person taking it but also for those who have to live with that person. It frees both sides from an unreasoning fear and allows red chestnut people to give, and their loved ones to receive, real comfort and security rather than waves of anxiety. This allows everyone to remain a little calmer and react better when there really is an emergency.

Case history: *Sara had tried for a baby for a long time before she became pregnant and from the day her son was born she was very protective of him. As he grew she was unable to let go or believe that he could take care of himself. Instead she was always anxious that something was going to happen to him and this anxiety affected her health as well as upsetting the boy, who began to doubt his ability to do normal everyday things such as walking to school and crossing the road.*

Red chestnut was the obvious remedy, backed up by white chestnut for the persistent worrying thoughts. Sara reported an immediate effect on her whole outlook, as well as her physical health. A long-standing digestive disorder cleared up within a couple of weeks, and she slept better than she had done for years.

Key symptoms: Fear that something awful will happen to a loved one. Over-concern for other people's welfare.
Associated problems: Intrusive fussing over other people's lives. Hypochondria about other people's symptoms.
Treatment goals: Encourage calm and rationality. Free the sufferer and his or her loved ones from unnecessary anxiety.

There is a white-flowered variety of rock rose, whose Latin name is Helianthemum appeninum. *This is very rare and should never by uprooted or disturbed in any way.*

ROCK ROSE

(*Helianthemum nummularium*)

The rock rose is an evergreen, hardy shrub which grows only about 7-10 centimetres high but spreads across the ground rapidly from year to year. The leaves are small and oblong, green on top and light grey and hairy on the underside. The flowers grow in loose terminal clusters from June to September, one or two at a time, and are a bright yellow.

PREPARATION: By the sun method.

INDICATIONS: Rock rose is the remedy for terror and panic. This is a far stronger and more intense fear than the mimulus fears and is characterized by symptoms such as severe shaking, hair standing on end, sweating and palpitations.

Examples of the kind of situations where the rock rose remedy might be called for include a sudden and terrifying *accident, a near escape from a car crash, a medical diagnosis that puts the patient in fear of his or her life, and a bad nightmare. All of these are conditions where the fright is so bad that it seems to freeze time and all the normal mental and physical functions. They are all also situations where many people would reach for the Rescue Remedy (see chapter 5), and of course one of the major elements in the Rescue Remedy composite is rock rose.

> *The remedies are not intended to replace normal medical care. With any accident, you should call for qualified medical assistance if you are in any doubt as to the seriousness of the injury. Do not move anyone who has been injured and cannot move unaided.*

The rock rose state can also be triggered by witnessing any of the above scenes. Terror and panic are notoriously contagious; thus if possible it's a good idea to offer the remedy to anyone in the vicinity so that any general air of panic can be eased. This will obviously benefit the victim of any accident as well, since in a calm atmosphere more can be accomplished more efficiently.

Rock rose is in many ways one of the most extreme of the remedies, in that it is a tool of last resort for when fear has caused the people being treated to lose control over their minds and emotions. Dr Bach referred to it as the 'remedy of emergency' and recommended its use in situations when there seems to be no more hope. By definition this means that the condition it treats is an acute, temporary one: there are no rock rose types, only rock rose states.

Like the Rescue Remedy, rock rose can be applied to the lips, wrists and temples if the person being treated is *unconscious or otherwise unable to swallow. Its action is to calm the nerves and restore rationality and will-power to the terrified person. The person's innate strength and the natural healing functions can then come back into play so that the cause of the terror can be addressed and overcome.

You should always consult a doctor if someone is unconscious for more than a few seconds. If the patient being treated is a child this is especially important, since even apparently minor knocks to the head can need urgent treatment.

CASE HISTORY: *Billy was a seven-year-old who had very bad nightmares after the unexpected death of his grandmother, of whom he had been particularly fond. Then he began to lose weight and suffer from a succession of minor illnesses. Rock rose was chosen for Billy because of the intensity of his fear and the dramatic effects it was having. After a week the nightmares* *stopped, and after a further few months of rock rose, with honeysuckle to help him let go of the past events that were preoccupying him, he made a complete recovery.*

Always follow the treatment instructions in chapter 3, especially when giving the remedies to young children, since the undiluted stock bottles contain almost pure brandy.

KEY SYMPTOMS: Sheer terror. Blind panic. A feeling of hopelessness and helplessness in the face of any calamity or terrifying situation, including nightmares.
ASSOCIATED PROBLEMS: Shock caused by fear (see also star of Bethlehem entry). Palpitations.
TREATMENT GOALS: Remove the terror and panic. Encourage calmness and courage in the face of fear.

ROCK WATER

As the lack of a Latin name indicates, rock water is the only one of the remedies that is not made from a flower or plant. Rather, it is water taken from any pure, natural spring or well which is open to the fresh air and sunshine and is known for its healing properties.
PREPARATION: By the sun method.
INDICATIONS: The rock water type can usefully be compared to the vervain, since both hold very definite opinions on everything under the sun. The difference is that whereas the vervain person will try to convince others to do as they do and believe the same things, rock water people are too concerned with achieving their own definitions of perfection to worry much about what others choose to do. Rather than directly persuading, they hope that others will see their shining example and change accordingly. As this suggests, there is a fair amount of spiritual pride in the rock water state, and an unhealthy tendency to concentrate on the self.

In their attempts to live according to their principles, rock water people tend to be very rigid in their outlook, and their desire for perfection leads them to push themselves beyond accepted limits. They are hard on themselves, denying themselves quite normal pleasures such as wine or chocolate as part of their effort to dominate and master their desires. They tend to follow set diets and strict exercise routines – spiritual as well as physical – in the attempt to reach the ideal they have set. When the practicalities of real life force them to 'cheat' by missing a yoga session or eating the wrong kind of food, they get upset and accuse themselves of weakness. In this way their unforgiving natures turn self-denial into self-martyrdom.

The rigidity of the rock water person's outlook may be reflected in a stiff and unbending body, causing *stiff joints and so on. The answer to their trouble is, quite simply, that they need to relax.

Rock water people in general have made a mistake in believing that discipline and will-power are enough in themselves to achieve perfection. Before they can really make progress spiritually they need to learn a little humility, and also how to forgive. In other words, they need to put aside their pride in strength and will-

Medical advice should always be sought, and followed, if you suspect that stiffness might be caused by arthritis or rheumatism. Remember that rock water is not a cure for arthritis or any other physical condition, and will not always be indicated when arthritis is present. Like all the remedies, it is given to ease an underlying mental or emotional state that may be contributing to the physical condition.

The flower remedies can be given in association with any other therapies. They will not interfere with the action of any other drug or painkiller.

power and be rather kinder to themselves. Once they learn to enjoy a moderate degree of physical pleasure they are free to stop concentrating on self-control – which means concentrating on the self – and can progress naturally towards the truly spiritual state of self-forgetfulness.

The remedy is given to allow this process to get underway. While leaving the high ideals of these people intact and giving them the strength to support their convictions in a fair and balanced way, it also enables them to regain the flexibility of mind that will allow them to learn from their mistakes, and the courage to abandon cherished theories if they are proved wrong. The quiet joy that they will then experience means that one of their fondest hopes can be realized: they will indeed become an example and a beacon for others to follow.

CASE HISTORY: *Gwynneth was in her late sixties, a woman of strict beliefs. She suffered from arthritis in her hands and severe cramps in her legs. She had been prescribed painkillers for the cramps, but had set herself a limit of three per day and sometimes endured great pain rather than break her own rule. Rock water was indicated to deal with Gwynneth's tendency to be too hard on herself. After a fortnight the cramps had eased and she did not need the painkillers any more. The arthritis too showed some improvement.*

KEY SYMPTOMS: Rigidity of mind. Self-denial coupled with self-obsession. Exaggerated idealism and perfectionism.
ASSOCIATED PROBLEMS: Rigidity of the body, stiffness, etc. Unforgiving nature. Inability to change beliefs or direction.
TREATMENT GOALS: Encourage greater flexibility in achieving ideals. Turn the gaze outward and away from the self.

SCLERANTHUS

(*Scleranthus annuus*)

Scleranthus is an annual plant that grows close to the ground along its tangled stems. It rarely grows more than about 7-10 centimetres high. Both the leaves and flowers are small and green, the exact shade depending on the soil the plant is rooted in. Scleranthus is found in sandy, well-drained soil and is in flower from June to August.

Preparation: By the sun method.

Indications: This is the remedy for people who find it impossible to decide which of two possible courses of action to take. They suffer from great uncertainty when they need to make decisions, and find that they veer constantly from one opinion to another without fixing on anything. Their indecision means they risk missing many of life's precious opportunities and also waste a great deal of time in dithering.

This indecision is the symptom of a deeper lack of certainty, as is shown by the fact that scleranthus people often suffer from mood swings. One minute they are crying tears of joy, the next weeping in despair; they feel full of energy one moment and the next they can hardly find the energy to get out of bed. Theirs have rightly been called 'grasshopper minds', since they hop from feeling to feeling, from thought to contradictory thought, never resting in one place long enough to put down roots.

Because their points of view change all the time, scleranthus people can be very unreliable. This is not because of any innate dishonesty, but is simply because they find it hard to concentrate. Their mood swings make them erratic and unpredictable, and their lack of firm principles means that they are likely to have changed their minds between promising something and actually carrying it out.

It is possible to confuse the scleranthus state with the cerato one, but there is a simple distinction. People in the cerato state do not have trouble making a decision but, having done so, doubts creep in and they start asking around for other people's opinions. Scleranthus people, on the other hand, don't ask for anyone else's opinions, and in fact try hard to keep their troubles to themselves. And of course they find it impossible to make up their own minds in the first place, which is not a problem cerato people have.

There are a few typical symptoms that people in a scleranthus state may complain of. Their lack of mental balance is mirrored by a lack of physical balance, and sufferers often report problems with travel sickness. When they are sick their symptoms tend to come and go, appearing vague and transitory. Relapses and remissions chase each other around as temperature and blood pressure rise and fall like the weather.

The remedy works to bring calm and certainty to the indecisive mind. Sufferers are able to take quick, correct decisions and act swiftly when necessary.

CASE HISTORY: *Norman was subject to mood swings. He had been diagnosed as suffering from a manic-depressive illness, for which he was undergoing treatment, but he also wanted to know if the flower remedies could help.*

Scleranthus was the automatic choice. As Norman believed his problems might be linked to a distressing incident in his childhood, honeysuckle was added to help him to focus on the present and leave the past behind.

Norman continued to take the remedies on and off along

In the case of mental illness, as with any other illness, you should never encourage or instruct someone to stop taking medication that has been prescribed for them by a qualified medical practitioner.
Anyone who feels that they might have a mental or physical illness should seek medical help.

with his orthodox treatment. He found them a great help in anchoring him more firmly in the present.

Key symptoms: Uncertainty and indecision. Inability to choose between two options. Erratic mood swings.

Associated problems: Sea-sickness, air-sickness etc.

Treatment goals: Change uncertainty into certainty, indecisiveness into decisiveness.

STAR OF BETHLEHEM

(*Ornithogalum umbellatum*)

Star of Bethlehem throws out long, thin leaves and a leafless central stalk from a single small bulb. These grow up to about 30 centimetres high and are dark green, the leaves having a thin white line down the middle. The flowers grow in branched clusters. They are shaped like a six-pointed star, white, with six stamens but no calyx, and appear in April and May.

Preparation: By the boiling method, using fully opened flowers.

Indications: Star of Bethlehem is one of the remedies included in the composite Rescue Remedy (see chapter 5). It is used to counteract the effects of any mental or physical shock: anyone who has been in or witnessed an *accident, or heard unexpected bad news of any kind, or experienced a sudden disappointment or scare can be helped with this remedy.

The remedies are not intended to replace normal medical care. With any accident, you should call for qualified medical assistance if you are in any doubt as to the seriousness of the injury. Do not move anyone who has been injured and cannot move unaided.

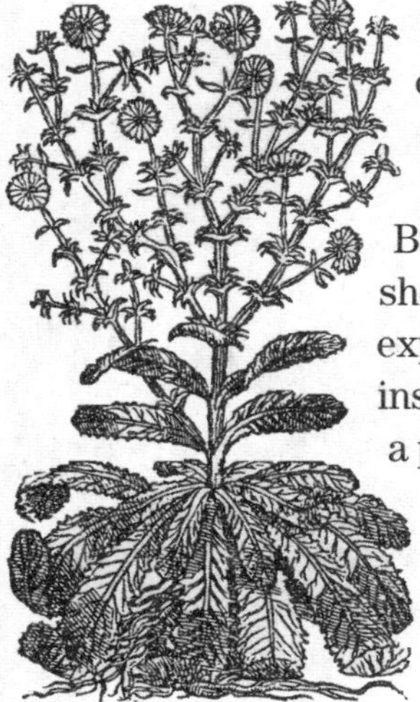

As its use in the Rescue Remedy suggests, it is often called on immediately after a shock has been experienced, when it can help the sufferer recover quickly and return to normal mental equilibrium. But it is also used months or even years after the shock occurred, because many people react to such an experience by repressing it and pushing it deep down inside. While this is effective in the short term it is not a permanent cure: eventually the repressed emotional state will come out, perhaps in the form of apparently unrelated physical symptoms, perhaps in the form of emotional problems, anxiety or stress.

Because it may not be obvious that a shock in the past is at the root of these other problems, anyone who is not responding to the remedies that seem to be indicated should be encouraged to talk about the past, and possible clues to a star of Bethlehem state noted. Question the person gently, since there may be a good reason why the shock has been repressed – bereavement, perhaps, or some distressing personal reverse. If there is indeed a shock that might be causing the other symptoms, star of Bethlehem can then be given and often the problem will suddenly start to disappear.

Although the shock can lie dormant for a long time, there is not really a star of Bethlehem type as such. On the other hand, everyone might need this remedy at some time or other in his or her life. Some practitioners make it the first remedy that a *newborn baby encounters, giving it to the breast-feeding mother so that she can pass it on in her

Remember when giving remedies to young children that stock bottles contain a large proportion of pure brandy. For this reason you should follow the treatment instructions in chapter 3, and if possible give the remedies diluted in water or some other drink. For suckling babies you can also follow the procedure described here.

milk. In this case both the mother and the child can benefit, since birth can be a traumatic experience for both of them.

The action of the remedy is to free the mind from the sudden freezing caused by a shock of any kind. The reasoning faculties can take over once more and the emotions are able to resume their normal flow. Once the effects of a shock are removed, the body's natural defences are able to work more efficiently. Pain is lessened, sorrow eased and the mind cleared for action and quick recovery.

CASE HISTORY: *Judith had been suffering from cystitis for years. She also felt she was becoming irritable with people around her.*

It seemed a straightforward case, and impatiens was prescribed for the irritation and impatience, plus vine for Judith's capable but sometimes domineering nature. She tried the remedies for a week or so, with no results. During a further consultation it emerged that her only child had developed Bright's disease, an inflammation of the kidneys, and had died. This had happened four years ago and the cystitis dated from then. For the shock she had suffered, star of Bethlehem was added, along with honeysuckle to help her get over the tragedy. The revised treatment was effective almost at once and the cystitis cleared up.

KEY SYMPTOMS: Shock, whether recent or in the past, and all the physical symptoms associated with it: vacant gaze, numbed thoughts, etc.

ASSOCIATED PROBLEMS: Possible psychosomatic symptoms due to repressed shock.

TREATMENT GOALS: Neutralize shock. Allow the normal mental, emotional and physical faculties to regain control.

SWEET CHESTNUT

(*Castanea sativa*)

The sweet chestnut is a deciduous tree that grows in open woodland and flowers in the summer, from June to August. Reaching up to 24 metres high, it is smaller than the more common white chestnut, and looks very different, with its glossy, toothed leaves and comparatively discreet flowers.

Both male and female blooms appear on the same tree: the male catkins are about 12.5 centimetres long, thin and yellow; the much smaller female flowers grow in clusters at the base of some of the catkins, and are enclosed in a rosette of bracts which later forms the tough envelope of the chestnut.

Preparation: By the boiling method.

Indications: Sweet chestnut is the remedy for the extremes of mental despair and anguish. It is for that state which lies beyond the simple discouragement of the gentian state or the pessimistic hopelessness of the gorse, beyond even the degree of mental torture felt by the agrimony person, and is used when sufferers are sure that they have reached the end of the road and face nothing but complete darkness ahead. The sweet chestnut state is one of ultimate loneliness and hopelessness reached after a long struggle, when the personality feels as if it has reached the limits of human endurance and is all but destroyed.

This state can be triggered in any number of ways, but it is particularly associated with crushing and irreversible losses or setbacks. The loss of a wife or husband, for example, can leave the surviving partner feeling that life is meaningless without the dead loved one; the death of a child is if anything even more difficult to bear.

Often the onset of despair is all the more sudden and terrible because of the courage that sufferers have shown in the face of terrible odds, for people in this state are usually strong characters who keep their troubles largely to themselves. Their very ability to resist for longer means that when they do succumb they do so in a more dramatic and apparently final way. The person who has been tireless in the search for a cure for cancer or some other life-threatening disease may feel nothing but despair and exhaustion at the end, when there seems no further possibility of cure. In all such situations the strength of the reaction indicates sweet chestnut as the appropriate remedy.

The remedy flushes out feelings of hopelessness and despair so that, however bad the situation might be, sufferers are able to go on hoping and trusting in the future. The strong characters of people of this type are strengthened further in their darkest hours, enabling them to go on to face their problems in full control of their emotions and actions. Thanks to the new knowledge of pain and anguish that they have gained they can be strong for other people too, so becoming real rocks to which others can cling. And as hope is needed before there can be any positive outcome, the return of hope can lead to the strangest triumphs – perhaps even to those sudden turns for the better that some would call miracles.

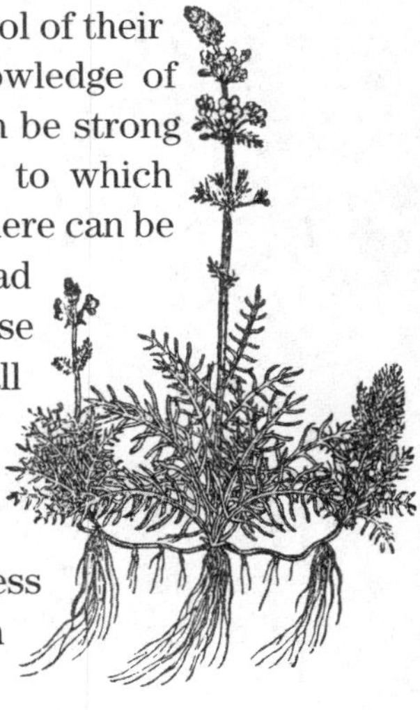

In those cases of terminal disease where there really is no way out, sufferers can face their futures with strength and clear-sightedness and are able to accept the things about which they can physically do nothing.

CASE HISTORY: *Ana was a survivor of a Nazi concentration camp who had lost her husband and son. The only thing that had kept her going was her love for her small daughter, whom she brought to England with her after the war.*

Although she had been a professional person before the war, in England Ana could obtain only the most menial work. Her health was poor, and by the time she came for a consultation she was at her wits' end, feeling that she had no future of any kind.

Sweet chestnut was tried. For a long time there was little change, but Ana persevered and at last there was some easing in her deep despair. She began to make plans again and to take real pleasure in the companionship of her daughter. The improvement continued, slowly and gradually, and although other remedies were added from time to time sweet chestnut was always the mainstay.

Key symptoms: Extremes of anguish and hopelessness. Absolute despair, loneliness and desolation. Dr Bach described this state as 'the dark night of the soul' when all hope is gone.

Associated problems: Despair is often kept to oneself so that the eventual collapse seems all the more irreversible.

Treatment goals: Restore hope and will to resist. Give strength to adjust and come to terms with inevitable change.

VERVAIN

(*Verbena officinalis*)

The perennial vervain grows up to about 60 centimetres high in sunny places such as roadsides and meadows. The toothed, bristly leaves grow in parallel on opposite sides of upright, tough and branching stems. The small flowers – ranging from white-mauve to violet – bloom from clustered buds at the end of slender spikes between July and September. The lower buds on each cluster appear first, then fade as the topmost buds burst open.

Preparation: By the sun method.

Indications: Vervain people have firm ideas and principles which they believe in utterly. They take their ideals very seriously, and once they have found what they consider to be a truth they immediately set to work to convert everyone around them. They are especially sensitive to the presence of injustice and may join societies and organizations dedicated to the righting of wrongs: they are the inveterate campaigners, fund-raisers and canvassers for this or that political or social cause.

Much of this is of course very positive and is to be encouraged. However, there are dangers faced by this type of person. Firm principles can become fixed so that tenacity on behalf of a cause turns into fanaticism, while the desire to persuade may become the inability to listen to other points of view. In addition, vervain people become so fired up that they put great stress on themselves. They try to do too much, driving themselves to extremes of mental activity and overworking beyond their physical limits. The result is that they soon find themselves unable to relax. A high level of emotional tension and insomnia can result as their minds run on ahead, forever thinking of the next thing that needs to be done or the next cause that needs to be defended.

They can go on like this for quite a long time, for vervain types tend to be very strong-willed and to have a great deal of courage when it comes to the causes they serve. But their perfectionism means that even their considerable reserves will never be enough to achieve everything they want as quickly as they want, and physical breakdown can result. If this happens, vervain types will tend to struggle on despite their symptoms, long after many people would have given up and taken to their beds. Of course, in the long run this very courage and strength of will only make things worse. Vervain people coming to a consultation or a doctor's surgery may have waited so long before doing this that they are in a very sorry state indeed.

If their condition prevents them from carrying on as normal, their highly-strung nature leads them to fret and fuss about how things will get done without their assistance. Like the quick-moving impatiens types, vervain types make very poor patients. Moreover, their very commitment and effort, if these make the illness worse, actually get in the way of the things they want to achieve.

The action of the vervain remedy is to ease

the tension and anxiety that such people are prone to. They are left just as firm and courageous when it comes to defending a cause, but their fanaticism is lessened so that they are able to listen to other opinions. In addition, they gain that very special type of courage displayed by those who are able to accept someone else's argument if it seems correct, instead of blindly continuing to assert the rightness of an incorrect conclusion.

Sleeping problems and stress-related illnesses, from which anyone who falls into a vervain state is likely to suffer, are also eased by the vervain remedy, which promotes a calm approach to life and its problems.

CASE HISTORY: *Sandra was a student in her twenties, heavily involved in student politics, who began to suffer from very bad headaches and mouth ulcers just before her end of year exams. Not surprisingly, she did not do as well as she had hoped, and she was told she would have to retake two of the papers. She was worried that the headaches would return and cause her to fail the retakes, which would mean failing the course.*

It was felt that the cause of Sandra's headaches and ulcers lay in her trying to do too much at once. Vervain was indicated to help her to relax. Mimulus was added for the fear that the headaches would return, and a bottle of Rescue Remedy (see chapter 5) was provided for times when worry about the exams might prove overpowering.

Sandra passed the two retake papers without any trouble.

KEY SYMPTOMS: Tension and stress. Extremes of mental and physical activity. Overcommitment to causes, bordering on fanaticism. Great sensitivity to injustice and unfairness.

Associated problems: Stress-related illnesses. Anxiety and insomnia. Overwork.
Treatment goals: Encourage a calm, reflective approach. Instil fair-mindedness and tolerance.

VINE

(*Vitis vinifera*)

The vine used for the remedy is the grape vine, a deciduous climbing shrub that can grow to more than 18 metres long. The stems are woody and the leaves are very deeply lobed and toothed. The flowers themselves are small, green and strongly perfumed, growing in dense clusters in the familiar shape of a bunch of grapes. At first each bloom is covered by a cap, which is pushed aside as the five stamens within ripen and grow.

Vine is not native to Britain. It grows in southern Europe, and blooms at different times of the year depending on the local climate.
Preparation: By the sun method.
Indications: Vine people have gifts far above the average. They are quick thinkers who are decisive and strong-willed enough to seem the natural leaders of any group in an emergency. Confidence comes naturally to them and this, along with an equally natural ambitiousness, means that they are often to be found in positions of power and responsibility, since their confidence in their own ability inspires trust in others.

However, as always there is a negative side to the vine type, and it is this side that the remedies are used to treat. For vine people's good qualities can themselves lead to their becoming domineering and inflexible, so that they insist on always getting their own way despite the opinions or needs of other people.

Instead of inspiring others to follow them they can end up demanding absolute, unquestioning obedience as a right and imposing their ideas on other people rather than trying to convince by reason and argument. Indeed, they are so certain that they are right that vine people rarely bother to argue at all. They do not really mind what others think as long as they do as they are told.

Vine types crave authority and power, not in order to achieve something else but as an end in itself. They can be ruthless in getting and holding on to power too, so that vine people are often seen as cruel and unfeeling. The domineering boss who terrifies the workforce with threats of redundancy and bawls out anyone who makes a slight mistake is an example of a negative vine person, as is the overpowering parent who rules the lives of his or her children with a discipline unsoftened by love.

Along with this desire for power comes a sort of aggressive pride. Vine people are sure they know better than anyone else and don't mind who knows it. Even when ill, a vine person is likely to tell the doctors and nurses what to do and even what the diagnosis and prognosis should be – and woe betide anyone who dares to contradict.

As the key words associated with the vine are inflexibility and rigidity of mind and behaviour, it is hardly surprising that they are especially prone to physical illnesses which manifest much the same underlying attitudes: *stiffness of the joints and other tension-related symptoms may be particularly common.

Stiffness may be caused by arthritis or rheumatism. Medical advice should always be sought, and followed, if you suspect that this might be the case. The flower remedies can be given in association with any other therapies prescribed for these conditions. They will not interfere with the action of any other drug or painkiller.

For someone who is a vine type or is in a vine state, the remedy is indicated to soften inflexibility and generally produce a less aggressive attitude. Instead of dominating through the brute force of personality and will-power, vine people can learn to offer guidance where once they issued orders. Their good qualities and leadership potential will actually be enhanced, since they will see the need to win respect and loyalty, and will understand the advantages to both leader and led of a more humane relationship.

CASE HISTORY: *Kenneth, the head of a large government department, had been ill for some time with a virus that left him very weak. He had been allowed indefinite sick leave and told to rest as much as possible, but he insisted on going back to work every time there was a slight improvement. This led to a series of relapses.*

He was an authoritarian boss, and his attitude towards his family and his doctor was much the same. Vine was given for this side of his nature, along with elm because of his worry that he was failing in his responsibilities, and olive to provide him with additional strength.

After the first few doses, Kenneth's attitude changed. He agreed to stay in bed until he was better, and for the first time acknowledged that his staff were capable of carrying on in his absence. In due course he made a full recovery.

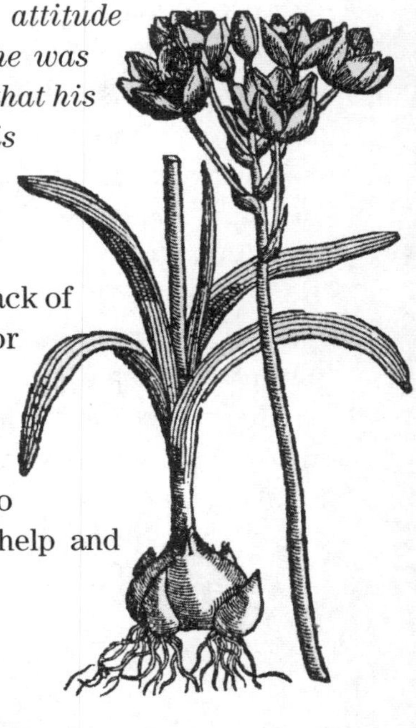

KEY SYMPTOMS: Desire to lead and dominate. Lack of flexibility. Aggressive pride and craving for power.

ASSOCIATED PROBLEMS: Tension and tension-related illnesses. Cruelty and lack of compassion.

TREATMENT GOALS: Soften domination into leadership by consent. Turn a tyrant into a help and guide to others.

WALNUT

(*Juglans regia*)

The walnut tree can grow up to 30 metres tall, but is usually around 15–18 metres high. The shoots and leaves are red-green, the leaves lanceolate and growing in opposing pairs. The grey bark is smooth on a young tree but as the years go by develops heavy furrows. This, together with the large bole and spreading crown, make the walnut tree a rugged, striking feature of many orchards.

The flowers appear in April or May, depending on the weather. The male catkins are green and chunky; the relatively insignificant female flowers appear on the same tree, in small groups or singly, and have pronounced calyxes wrapped tightly around yellow-green stigmas.

Preparation: By the boiling method, using young leafy shoots, with female flowers only attached – the male catkins are not used.

Indications: Each individual has a path to pursue through life, yet it is all too easy for outside influences to lead people astray. Walnut is the remedy to deal with these influences, whatever shape they come in: interfering friends, circumstances, ideas, propaganda, or simply the ties of the past. People are said to be in the walnut state when they are inclined to pay too much heed to such things, becoming oversensitive to ideas and opinions to which they would not normally pay any attention.

Walnut is indicated whenever there is some change coming in people's lives. This can range from babies cutting their first teeth, to puberty, childbirth and the menopause, to leaving home, changing jobs, retiring or taking momentous decisions such as getting married or divorced or becoming involved in a new religion. Any change in one's life or circumstances entails leaving something behind, and as the link-breaking remedy walnut helps those who are unsettled by this.

For example, if you are on the verge of moving abroad you might have a hundred reasons for doing so – a better climate, a nice house, a new relationship, a well-paid job and so on. Yet you may still hesitate to take the final step because of ties to old memories and familiar places – ties that normally seem unimportant. It may even be a foolish remark someone makes about the dangers of travel that holds you back, despite your desire to move on. In both cases walnut acts as a kind of shield against these interferences and lets a person make a clear-headed judgement and a fresh start.

People in the walnut state should not be confused with scleranthus types, who are unable to decide whether or not to take some step. Walnut people do not usually have any problem taking decisions, and have definite plans for their lives that they are busy carrying out. Walnut is only required on those occasions when their resolve falters. It helps to maintain the course of a life and promote positive change.

CASE HISTORY: *Susannah was sleeping badly and had been diagnosed as having irritable bowel syndrome. She was about to go up to university to study Classics, mainly because her father had studied this subject and wanted her to do the same. She wanted to study Modern Languages instead, but was afraid of his reaction, as he was a rather domineering man.*

To help her break away from her father's influence, walnut was prescribed, along with mimulus to help counteract the fear of what he would say. As soon as she told her father of her decision to drop Classics – he took it quite calmly, after a little persuasion – the bowel problems cleared up and Susannah began sleeping properly. Instead of dreading university life, she began to look forward to it.

KEY SYMPTOMS: Oversensitivity to outside influences. Reluctance to change caused by past ties.

ASSOCIATED PROBLEMS: Temporary domination

by a strong personality. Any of the many milestones in life, from being born to going into retirement.

Treatment goals: Free the person from interference. Allow the course of life to resume. Aid positive changes.

WATER VIOLET

(*Hottonia palustris*)

The water violet is named for the colour of its flowers – pale violet or lilac with a yellow centre – rather than for any connection with the woodland violet. It is actually a member of the primrose family.

The plant grows in still or slow-moving fresh water. Most of the leaves are submerged, but a fine rosette lies on the surface, where it helps to keep the flowering stem vertical. The stem itself is bare of leaves, with the flowers blooming towards the top, any time in May or June.

Preparation: By the sun method.

Indications: Water violet people are among the most talented and intelligent and also the quietest of people. They are natural aristocrats, self-contained, independent and keeping themselves to themselves. Disliking and avoiding if possible crowds and noisy parties, they prefer their own company or quiet evenings spent with one or two close friends, and they keep their own counsel. This is true even when they are ill, for they will suffer in silence and never consider telling other people about their aches and pains. They are blessed with refined tastes and good judgement, and are quiet and sure in their movements, completely at home in their bodies, with an easy grace and poise that set them apart from their fellows.

Well-adjusted water violet types are respected and revered when they are in positions of power. Their ability to see through the fuss and panic of everyday activity makes them the still centre of many a storm. As they will not interfere directly in the work of subordinates but seek to guide gently and quietly, they are much-valued bosses.

Water violet people, then, are highly developed personalities, superior in many ways to most of humanity. As one might expect, this very superiority can cause problems. At times their detachment can make them appear indifferent to the fate of others, and their consciousness of superiority can easily encourage them to act in a condescending, proud manner. If other people do not respond to the indirect promptings of water violet managers, they are likely to express their disapproval by simply withdrawing their attention. But in the end it is the water violet who suffers when this happens, since withdrawing too far can bring loneliness, and with it a great deal of unhappiness.

Pride carried too far can also result in physical problems. The normally fluid water violet can *stiffen up and suffer from tension in the muscles and joints as a result of too great a swing towards the extremes of mental reserve and rigidity.

Stiffness may be caused by arthritis or rheumatism or a number of other conditions, some of them serious. If there is any doubt about this or any other symptoms, medical advice should always be sought.

The flower remedies can be given in association with any drugs or other therapies that might be prescribed for arthritis and rheumatism.

When the negative aspects of the water violet type are emphasized, the remedy is there to break down the brittle barrier that has cut separated the sufferer from the world of everyday fears and aspirations. Restored to a greater sense of sympathy with other people, water violet types are able to translate their great talents and abilities into great deeds, and their poise and intelligence become a source of hope and renewal to those around them.

CASE HISTORY: *Samuel was the typical water violet boss – well liked because he didn't interfere, never raised his voice and was quietly and unobtrusively efficient. He resorted to the remedies for a stiff neck which was stopping him from sleeping.*

Water violet was prescribed, and also rock water because he admitted to being hard on himself on the rare occasions when he made a mistake at work.

When Samuel reported back it was to say that the stiffness had gone. He was also finding it easier to relax generally.

KEY SYMPTOMS: Pride and aloofness, often leading to loneliness.
ASSOCIATED PROBLEMS: Mental and physical rigidity.
TREATMENT GOALS: Encourage the self-reliant person to open up to others. Temper pride with sympathy.

WHITE CHESTNUT

(*Aesculus hippocastanum*)

The white (or horse) chestnut grows up to 30 metres high and provides two remedies: white chestnut and chestnut bud. While the bark on the trunk and the sturdy main branches is grey-brown and scaly, the smaller twigs holding the sticky buds are smooth in winter. The buds open in April to reveal drooping leaflets that gradually fan out and level off. The terminal buds also shoot up into dense, upright conical shapes made up of many small flowers on stalks, white and spotted with red and yellow.
PREPARATION: By the sun method.
INDICATIONS: The white chestnut state is perhaps the commonest cause of sleeplessness, for it comes at those times when unwanted thoughts revolve endlessly in the head, driving all chance of sleep away. And of course this condition is not confined to the night hours: nagging worries like these can break into the mind at any time, stopping sufferers from concentrating on other things and keeping them preoccupied with the

negative at the expense of the positive. People in this state can be so distracted that they seem to lose their sense of hearing, not answering when others talk to them. They might become accident-prone simply because they are unable to keep their attention on things of the moment.

Sometimes the unwanted thoughts are not so much worries as re-runs of what the person has been doing. It might be an argument with a friend that took place hours ago which keeps replaying in the head, with endless variations on what should have or might have been said. After a day of strenuous effort the thoughts might be connected with work: accountants add up columns of figures; shop assistants mentally stack and re-stack the same shelves; typists type the same imaginary memos over and over again.

People in the white chestnut state have literally become victims of their own minds. They have lost control over their mental processes so that the physical need to rest, relax and fall asleep is overridden by the mind's desire to go on working things out. In extreme cases, where the state becomes semi-permanent, sufferers can be subject to chronic insomnia and nervous headaches, or may grind their teeth as if hoping that firmly closed jaws will be able to still the chattering of their thoughts.

Even when the case is not as severe as this, the constant revolution of intrusive thoughts spoils the present and makes each day a trial. Sufferers are unable to live their lives properly and feel trapped by their minds.

White chestnut is the remedy to relieve this distressing state. It quickly banishes the unwanted mental arguments and worries, leaving the mind cool and clear and at peace with itself. The sufferer is able to think about any problems in a constructive way and to find real and satisfying solutions to worries. Most importantly, the way is free to think about the present and savour each moment to the full, free of interruption.

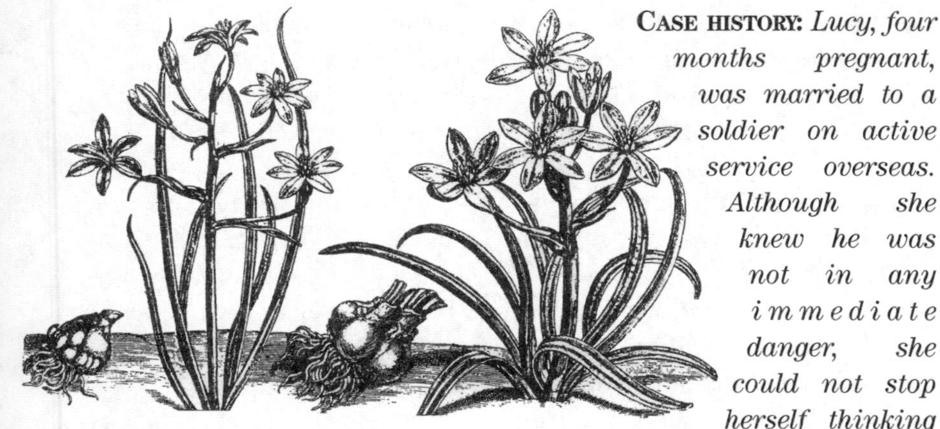

CASE HISTORY: *Lucy, four months pregnant, was married to a soldier on active service overseas. Although she knew he was not in any immediate danger, she could not stop herself thinking what might happen if his unit got to an area where there was fighting. She became quite ill with worry and lack of sleep.*

White chestnut was given for the repetitive and unwanted thoughts, and red chestnut to get her fears for her husband's safety into perspective. Ten days later Lucy reported a definite improvement.

KEY SYMPTOMS: Unwanted and persistent worries and other repetitive thoughts. Mental arguments.
ASSOCIATED PROBLEMS: Insomnia, headaches and tiredness. Inability to concentrate on the tasks and pleasures of the moment.
TREATMENT GOALS: Flush out the unwanted thoughts. Leave the mind at peace, able to think clearly about problems and let go of them once they are solved.

WILD OAT

(*Bromus ramosus*)

Wild oat is a kind of wild grass which grows from 50 centimetres to 2 metres high and is commonly found in English woods, hedgerows and wasteland. Towards the top of the main stem the plant throws out hair-fine branches, either singly or in pairs. Each branch carries two, three or more pale spikes of overlapping scales, containing the flower, which blooms in July or August.

Wild oat can be hard to distinguish from the many other grasses of the same genus which look like it, and the problem is not made easier by the fact that there are other similar plants that are not even part of the same family.

*The lesser hairy brome-grass (*Bromus benekenii*) is rare and should not be disturbed. Unlike the* Bromus ramosus, *its branches of flower heads are thrown out in clusters of more than two at a time.*

PREPARATION: By the sun method.

INDICATIONS: Wild oat is the remedy to help people who find themselves uncertain as to which path to take in life. These people just cannot seem to find their niche. They will in all likelihood have tried many things but have not found anything that they feel able to give themselves to wholeheartedly. These are the people who always seem to be starting new interests, yet never carry any of them through with enough conviction to make a go of them. They may try a large number of wildly different careers, going from trainee nurse to shop manager to receptionist to reporter without finding any of these jobs satisfying or fulfilling enough to hold them for long.

Because wild oat people usually do not have trouble making up their minds, they can become very frustrated and depressed when they are suddenly unable to come to a decision about something as important as what direction their future should take. This is made all the worse by the fact that they usually have a genuine desire to do something worthwhile with their lives, and feel all the time that they are missing their chances and wasting their talents. The longer the situation continues the worse they feel about it, and frustration can tip over into despair after repeated efforts have ended unhappily.

The remedy acts to give sufferers a chance to take stock of themselves, where they are and where they want to be. It gives them patience and perseverance so that they can try a little harder for a little longer. Gradually and subtly, it encourages the union of thought and intuition that is often all that is needed for a breakthrough. The path ahead is suddenly seen clearly – as if it had been there all the time but hidden by too much misdirected effort – and the talented individual can at last begin to live a life filled with happiness and achievement.

At a lower level, a temporary version of the negative wild oat state can strike any normally decisive person who suddenly finds it difficult to make an important decision that involves a future direction. Superficially this state can be confused with the scleranthus one, for both are states of uncertainty where decisions are difficult to make. The difference is that whereas the scleranthus state makes it hard to take even trivial decisions, the wild oat condition affects people who are decisive and clear-sighted in most things. The difference is one of degree: indecisiveness in trivial matters against a lost feeling when faced with the most important decisions in life.

Case history: *Susie was a German teacher working for a business training centre which arranged courses and paid her a monthly salary. A friend had suggested that she leave to work freelance, so making more money and having the chance to travel and work abroad, but Susie was worried by the lack of security involved.*

Susie was not having any trouble taking everyday decisions, so scleranthus didn't seem to be indicated. Instead, wild oat was given. Within a few days she knew what she wanted to do, and was able to go ahead and do it.

KEY SYMPTOMS: Uncertainty about which direction to pursue in life.
ASSOCIATED PROBLEMS: Frustration. Aimless drifting from career to career, coupled with the desire to achieve great things.
TREATMENT GOALS: Help sufferers find their true vocations.

WILD ROSE

(*Rosa canina*)

The wild rose is the dog rose, probably one of the most beautiful of the remedy flowers. Ranging in colour from white to a deep rose-pink, the flowers are made up of five heart-shaped petals around a centre with prominent stamens and styles, and grow singly or in groups of three or four. The flowers appear on the thorny shrub from June to August.
PREPARATION: By the boiling method.

In practice it is extremely difficult to distinguish the wild rose used for the remedy from the other varieties of wild rose, so preparation of this remedy is probably best left to the experts.

INDICATIONS: Resignation and apathy are the key words used to describe the negative wild rose state. Whatever the situation a person in this state is in, there is no energy or will to change it, simply a weary resignation. Illness, boredom, failed relationships, even domestic violence or bullying are all borne with a shrug of the shoulders and a weary 'I'll just have to get used to it'. This happens even where the cure for the problem is obvious to everyone except the wild rose person, for this is someone who has surrendered entirely and has accepted life and its consequences with meek contentment. At times he or she may believe that any effort is doomed and that as a result there is no point in making one – but this apathetic state of mind is of course not as extreme as the pessimistic hopelessness of the gorse state.

The apathy of people in this state spills over into the way they act and speak. Their voices often take on a flat, expressionless quality, while they walk around with drooping shoulders and dragging steps, with no semblance of vitality. All in all, they do not make very entertaining company.

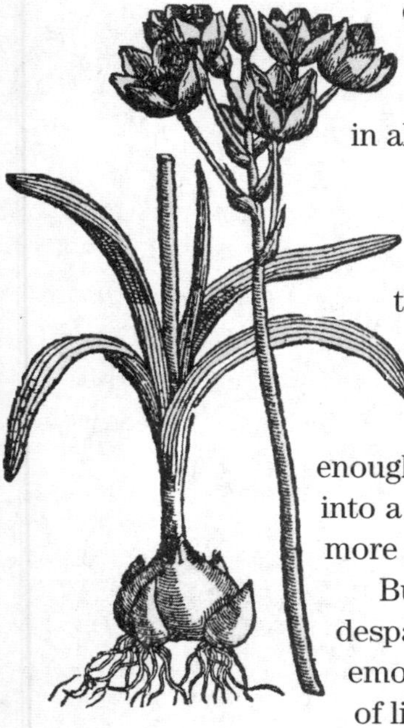

Often this state, while fundamentally the same, will appear less dramatic than the description above might suggest. The apathy in this case will be vaguer, more general and almost easy-going. These are the people who drift through life as if it has nothing much to do with them, saying if asked that they are happy enough with things the way they are. They fall easily into a monotonous routine and make no effort to find more interesting ways of living.

But whether these people say that they are in despair or content with their lot, their colourlessness, emotional aridity and lack of desire for a better way of life are sure symptoms of the wild rose state. And in all cases the problem is a self-created one, nourished and maintained by the wild rose person's ailing personality.

The remedy acts in these cases to restore such people's zest for living. They begin to see that there is the potential for change in even the most unpromising circumstances, and they can start to take purposeful action to find a cure for their illnesses, escape boredom, change careers and relationships and generally begin to create something worthwhile and interesting out of their moribund lives. This is not to say that they lose their ability to let things happen to them, or become any less easy-going. It's just that they are able to take action if and when it is needed – and if they choose to drift, they do so not by just giving in but in full consciousness and with increased and genuine delight in the ability to let things happen.

As their vitality increases, so they begin to have a more positive effect on those around them. Far from being the emotional drags they were, in their positive state wild rose people can turn out to be the centre of much happiness and a wide circle of admiring friends.

CASE HISTORY: *Martin was a teenager with fairly severe acne. His mother had suggested he see a doctor, or try dietary changes or aromatherapy, but Martin had simply said he couldn't be bothered. He seemed to have much the same attitude to the rest of his life too.*

Martin's mother was advised to try her son with wild rose to counteract his apathy, as well as crab apple to cleanse his system and to be applied externally.

When Martin saw a small improvement in the acne, his attitude immediately became more positive. He was keen to make the changes to his lifestyle that would minimize the problem, and in time the acne faded almost completely.

KEY SYMPTOMS: Resignation and apathy.
ASSOCIATED PROBLEMS: Lack of energy and mental activity. May take a long time to throw off trivial illnesses, due to lack of desire for improvement.
TREATMENT GOALS: Reawaken an interest in and zest for life. Encourage purposeful action and simple joy in being alive.

WILLOW

(*Salix vitellina*)

The willow used for the remedy is the yellow willow, also known as the golden osier, which can be distinguished from the many other types by the way its twigs turn bright yellow in winter. Otherwise the bark is grey-brown and thick, with deep fissures. The lanceolate leaves grow up to 10 centimetres long and are a glossy green on top and silky below. The long, thin catkins appear along with the leaves in May. They are the same shade of green.
PREPARATION: By the boiling method.
INDICATIONS: The willow remedy is called for whenever there is resentment and bitterness

and the kind of self-pity that has people blaming everyone but themselves for things going wrong. People in a willow state are introspective and entirely wrapped up in themselves and their needs and difficulties. They resent any luck or good fortune that comes to others and feel hard done by, as if fate is conspiring against them. 'Why should that person enjoy health – or happiness – or wealth', they say, 'and not me?'

As you might expect, willow people are not good company. They are forever complaining and moaning and tend to be irritable wet blankets. They seem to enjoy, in their peculiarly morose way, spreading doom and gloom all around them. They only take an interest in other people's lives or events in general when they can see an opportunity to run them down and contrast their own ill fortune with the undeserved luck of others.

Willow types are like emotional black holes: they suck in all the sympathy and help they can attract, but never does a single gleam of gratitude or simple fellow feeling radiate back out towards other people. They take all the time, and seem to think they have some kind of right to go on doing so. When they are ill they are just the same, grumbling and moaning constantly, satisfied by nothing. And when they start to recover they tend to deny that it is happening for as long as possible.

Someone in a true willow state of mind, then, is not very pleasant to know. But the truth is that almost everyone at one time or another falls into a willow state where self-pity and bitterness lead to a feeling of resentment towards everyone else. During an illness, for example, it is common to feel rather too sorry for oneself. The problem is that this kind of feeling can act as an excuse for not trying anything new, so that whole days – sometimes whole years – can pass in wasted, negative thinking and morose sulkiness.

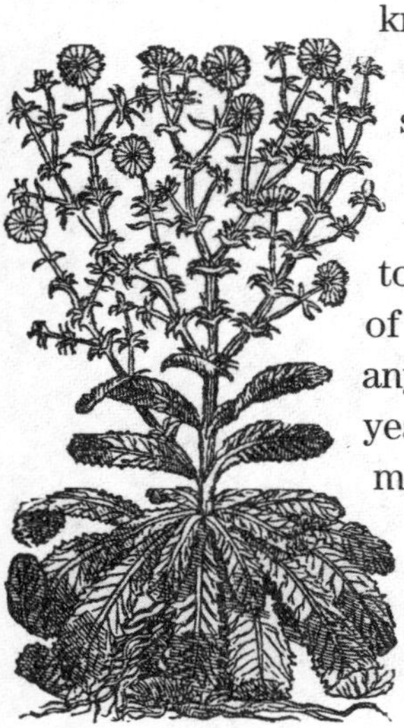

Fortunately the remedy is there to reverse the negative willow state and renew these people's optimism and faith in themselves and their ability to see the good side of things. Able to take the knocks of fate on the chin without blaming others who may have been more successful, they can pick up the threads of their lives and keep worldly ideas of success and failure in proportion: this in itself is no mean achievement.

CASE HISTORY: *At the age of fifty-one, Marian was one of twenty-five people made redundant from employment in a shoe factory. Another forty kept their jobs, and Marian grew very resentful of this. Some of the people still at the factory had been her friends for years, but over the next few weeks she managed to pick fights with nearly all of them. This left her feeling even more alone. She could see that her behaviour was not helping but was powerless to stop it, and she was beginning to blame herself for the whole situation.*

Because Marian's bitterness and resentment were largely introspective, the main remedy needed was willow. She was also given pine to deal with the feelings of guilt arising from her behaviour. The third remedy selected was holly, because her normally sulky resentment had at times manifested itself in angry, envious outbursts against her friends and former colleagues.

Marian gradually came to terms with her redundancy and started looking for another job. After a year, she found work with an old schoolfriend who had set up a workshop making leather goods. This was more creative and interesting than her previous job, and in later years she was able to see her redundancy as a blessing in disguise.

KEY SYMPTOMS: Resentment, sulkiness, bitterness, self-pity and ingratitude.
ASSOCIATED PROBLEMS: Introspective, negative thoughts of all kinds. Tearfulness.
TREATMENT GOALS: Lift the person out of the rut of negativity. Encourage a more positive, even-minded approach to life and to other people.

CHAPTER 5

RESCUE REMEDY

The most famous of all the flower remedies is not properly speaking a remedy at all, but a mixture of five different remedies in a stock bottle. The Rescue Remedy, as it is known, is formulated to deal with the effects of all kinds of *accidents, traumas and emergencies. It works to calm the shock and fear that follow any unexpected calamity, pain or misfortune. This can be anything from a child's grazed knee or a minor fright, to a bereavement or major accident. By removing the emotional paralysis the Rescue Remedy allows the body and mind to recover more quickly so that the natural healing process can begin as soon as possible.

Rescue Remedy is not intended to replace normal medical care. With any accident, you should call for qualified medical assistance if you are in any doubt as to the seriousness of the injury. Do not move anyone who has been injured and cannot move unaided.

As well as treating the victims of an accident, Rescue Remedy can also help calm relatives and onlookers. And of course, if you are busy treating others at the scene of an accident, don't forget to save some for yourself.

Rescue Remedy can also be used for the sudden bout of nerves that you can experience when you are about to face a challenge of some kind – an examination, perhaps, or maybe an operation. Bad travellers have found it helps to deal with the fear of flying, and some women have reported that it has helped them cope with childbirth: before the birth (calming anticipatory fears), during the process of labour (coping with stress and pain), and immediately after the baby has been born (recovering from shock and great physical effort).

The five remedies that make up the Rescue Remedy are as follows:

star of Bethlehem, to help to take care of the initial shock;
cherry plum, to counteract any feelings of desperation;
rock rose, to ease the sense of panic or terror;
impatiens, to soothe stress and tension; and
clematis, to counteract the rather confused, light-headed feeling that often comes just before a loss of consciousness.

See chapter 4 for a detailed description of each of these five remedies.

Any of the remedies described can of course be given in isolation or in any other combination, as long as they are available and the alternative composite is felt to be more appropriate. The advantage of Rescue Remedy is that it can be carried about in a single bottle and contains something to help all forms of shock and trauma.

Rescue Remedy is available ready-mixed for you, so you do not need to buy the five individual remedies if you do not want to.

DOSAGE

Rescue Remedy is used at double the strength of the other stock preparations. So instead of two drops, add four drops of the stock concentrate to a glass of water, and then take frequent sips every few minutes as required.

If there is no water available, the remedy can be added to any available drink. If there is no liquid of any kind in which to dilute the stock, a few drops can be placed on the tongue direct from the stock bottle – although you need to remember that pure brandy is used to preserve the stock remedy and so in undiluted form it can be rather too strong for some tastes.

If the person being treated is unable to swallow, a few drops of the remedy, diluted or undiluted, can be applied to the lips, or dabbed behind the ears and on the wrists and temples, where it will still have a healing effect.

You can use the Rescue Remedy to help minor cuts and grazes as well, although in this case you should be sure to dilute it first, because undiluted it will sting. For very minor *burns, diluted Rescue Remedy can be applied and allowed to evaporate so that the skin cools. This helps calm the affected person, allowing the natural healing process to start as soon as possible. Similarly, a cold compress can be used to relieve pain and swelling. Simply add four drops of the Rescue Remedy to some cold water; then dip a clean, sterile cloth in the water and place on the affected area.

If a burn is anything but very minor, or the sufferer is in shock as the result of a burn, you should call for medical assistance as soon as possible. Only completely sterile cloths and dressings should ever be applied to burns.

See chapter 3 for detailed instructions on how to make up a treatment bottle.

You can also make up a *treatment bottle using Rescue Remedy stock. Use four drops per 30 millilitre treatment bottle, and add other remedies in the normal dosage (two drops per remedy) as required.

However, in practice you will hardly ever need to use Rescue Remedy in a treatment bottle, because if there is time to make up such a bottle there is also time to consider which of the five remedies in the Rescue Remedy is actually needed. If you do this, the sharper focus you achieve will be more effective in the long run, as well as more economical. Rescue Remedy is really for those occasions when something is needed at once to cope with a sudden and pressing emotional state. It should not be taken as a cure-all. Indeed, if you rely on it too much you may only be masking some underlying problem, instead of dealing with it once and for all.

Rescue Remedy is useful to have in an emergency, but if you find yourself constantly relying on it this is a sign that you should take a good look at yourself to see if there might be some underlying cause for the constant emergencies that you seem to be faced with. If you can treat this underlying problem, you might be able to stop running to the first aid kit all the time.

RESCUE REMEDY CREAM

As well as Rescue Remedy in liquid form, you can also buy a specially formulated Rescue Remedy cream. This consists of a lanolin-free, homoeopathically prepared base, to which the mother tinctures of the five remedies detailed on page 124 have already been added, along with crab apple for its cleansing power. The cream does not contain any animal fats.

Rescue Remedy cream comes into its own with external injuries, such as cuts, grazes, insect bites, rashes and sunburn, which it helps to soothe and heal in a gentle yet effective way. It can also be applied to help prevent blisters and chafing prior to cross-country rambling, playing sports, or running. After the event it is equally useful, for it can be massaged into stiff shoulders and legs to help deal with the effects of any overexertion.

CHAPTER 6

HEALING YOURSELF

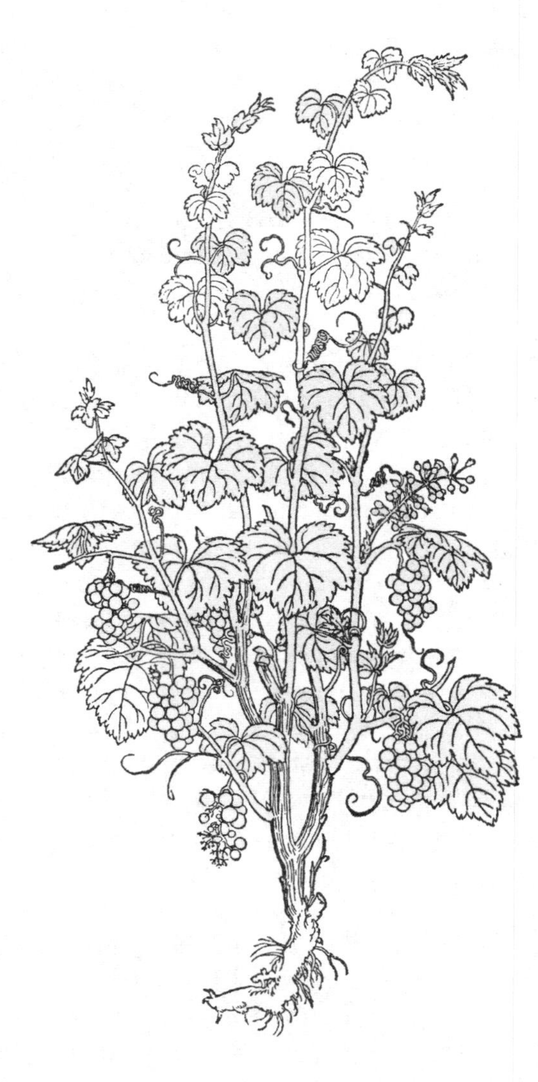

'Heal yourself' sums up the whole philosophy of the flower remedies. They are so simple to use that anyone can treat him or herself, given a little perseverance and the patience necessary to pinpoint the remedies required.

Perhaps it is surprising then that many people find it harder to be objective about their own needs than they do about those of other people. Nevertheless, self-treatment can be successful, and this chapter aims to give you some useful hints to help you pinpoint the remedies that you need.

TYPE REMEDIES

The first stage to treating yourself successfully with the flower remedies is to decide which remedy best corresponds to your personality type. This is perhaps best done when you are in your usual frame of mind and not especially troubled by any unusual mental state, because the type remedy is by definition the one that defines your basic character and the way you are normally.

If you look through the entries for the remedies in chapter 4, you will find many descriptions of types of people. Many of these may appear to be negative, but in each case there is a positive side as well. For example, vine people are described as being at times overpowering, harsh and aggressive. All of these are negative characteristics; but the same people are also described, in their positive incarnation, as natural leaders, full of self-confidence and never shirking responsibility. If you recognize yourself in this description, vine may well be your type remedy. Saying this doesn't mean that you are a dyed-in-the-wool bully or that you will rise effortlessly to positions of command, as of right. All it signifies is that your underlying character traits lead you to be dominant, and that when your personality is out of balance the negative traits that you have are often responsible for the problem. Once you know your type remedy you will have a good idea where to start looking for the cause of any particular problem with which you want the remedies to help. To help you pinpoint your type remedy you might like to try the following techniques:

1. Write down all your good points and main strengths. Then note down what you think are the weaknesses that arise from those strengths. For example, if you consider your fortitude and ability to keep going in the face of overwhelming odds to be a strength, but feel that at times you work yourself too hard, oak might be your type remedy.
2. Imagine yourself in various situations – at a party, for example, or attending a business meeting or giving a speech, and write down what your responses would be. Do you feel certain that you will make a mess of the speech, or are you excited at the thought of letting your audience know exactly what you think? In the former case, your lack of confidence might lead you to look at larch as a possible type remedy; in the latter, your eagerness to persuade others of the rightness of your point of view could indicate that you are the vervain type.
3. Consider what qualities you feel you lack. Would you like to be more decisive? If so, take a close look at the scleranthus and cerato types to see which one best fits you. Or perhaps you wish you could mix more easily with other people. Water violet might be indicated if you tend to hold yourself aloof, but if shyness is the root cause of the problem then you might be more the mimulus type.
4. If all else fails, ask someone else to tell you in all honesty what your good and bad qualities are – and don't get upset if the answer is not as flattering as you might wish.

Whether you use all or none of these techniques, the important thing is to be honest with yourself. Some of the descriptions might appeal to you more than others – but it will do you no good trying to mimic a

characteristic that you do not have. Remember that all the types have positive and negative characteristics, and you can be a better and finer human being without finding it necessary to pretend to be something you are not – in fact, the pretence is one of the things you should be trying to strip away.

One last thing: it is fairly common for people to read through the descriptions of the remedies and quickly come to the conclusion that they need all of them. Don't be disappointed or downhearted if you have this experience. As you will see when we look at mood remedies (see below), you are probably right in supposing that at one time or another you might have benefited from any one of the thirty-eight remedies. The type remedy, however, is the common thread that runs through your life. And once again the secret to successful self-diagnosis lies in being honest with yourself.

MOOD REMEDIES

While the type remedy relates to the basic characteristics that define your personality and the way you live your life, mood remedies are those that are indicated at particular times and, as the name suggests, reflect transitory mental and emotional states rather than persistent attitudes. Not all of the thirty-eight remedies are type remedies – it would be hard to imagine a star of Bethlehem type, for instance, since this remedy is for shock – but all of them can be mood remedies.

Just as it is hard to be objective when determining your type remedy, so diagnosing your own moods and temporary states can be difficult too. This is especially the case when the mood you are in tends to cloud your judgement anyway; for example, when you are depressed or upset or angry.

Perhaps the easiest way to get round this is to start by listing the remedies that you think might apply to your problem. For instance, if you are having trouble sleeping, your first thought might be that it is because you are overtired (olive) and finding it hard to switch off (white chestnut).

This may well be a correct diagnosis, but in order to be sure you need to take things a little further – just as you would if you were prescribing for someone else (see chapter 7). Ask yourself if there is some underlying cause that would better describe the emotions you are feeling. Are the worrying thoughts caused by a sudden fear that you may not be able to cope with all your responsibilities at work? If so, add elm to the list. And have these doubts been brought on by the unreasonable criticisms of your overbearing boss? If you answer 'yes', you might be going through a temporary centaury state.

Once you have gone a little deeper into things, you may find that the remedies required to treat the underlying cause are very different from the ones that a superficial glance at the effect might seem to indicate. In the last example given above, you would certainly end up by striking olive off the list, and quite possibly white chestnut and elm too.

To sum up, then, the mood remedies – all of the thirty-eight remedies – can apply to all sorts and conditions of people from time to time. Even the most decisive of vines may sometimes vacillate and call for scleranthus; even the quietest and most self-possessed water violet may grow mad with grief or anger and need the help of cherry plum.

TREATING YOURSELF

Once you have determined your type remedy (see above) you are well on your way to determining the remedies that you will need to help you overcome many of the problems and states that you encounter. Knowing that you are a particular type – clematis, for example – means that you can safely look at that remedy first whenever you are suffering from some medium- to long-term emotional or psychological problem, or from a physical illness that may be linked to it – and if clematis is your type you will be on the lookout for evidence that you have been day-dreaming and perhaps need a gentle tug to bring you back to present reality.

Whenever the problem is more than a transitory one, then, you should start your diagnosis with your type remedy. But does this mean that the type remedy should always be included in the prescription as a matter of course? And what if the problem is only a temporary one?

The answer to both questions is that each case should be judged objectively and purely on its merits. For example, if you suffer from a sudden and unexpected migraine after a day out shopping with friends, you would be right to look first at your type remedy for a clue. If you are an impatiens person, have you been secretly fuming all day while the people you are with dawdle at shop windows and take forever to decide which of two near-identical items to buy? Or are you the typical willow, watching with smouldering resentment and self-pity as your wealthier friend buys all the things that you would like but can't afford? In these cases, clearly, the type remedy gives an indication as to where to look first.

But there will be other situations where your type remedy plays no appreciable part. Perhaps you have indeed been displaying all the impatient irritation of an impatiens or the resentment of a willow, but you are normally a rather apathetic wild rose person who is quite unused to these feelings. This doesn't mean that you have suddenly changed type – only that in this case what you need is not necessarily the type remedy, but rather the remedy for the specific emotion that you are actually feeling. After all, it is perfectly characteristic of human beings to act out of character from time to time. Don't we say that we aren't quite ourselves, when we are only feeling unwell?

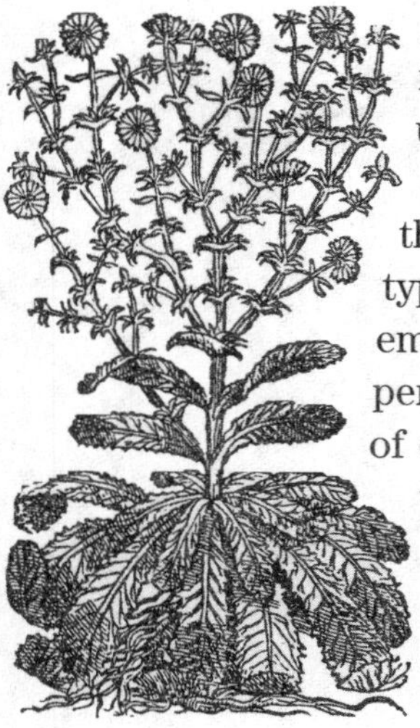

Lastly, there are of course those simple states that everyone can fall into – such as tiredness after long study, or the discouragement felt at a minor setback. Here the appropriate remedies – olive for the first and gentian for the second – could be taken at once and almost as a matter of course. With such straightforward moods there is no need for the making up of treatment bottles of carefully selected type remedies. The watchword once more is simplicity.

For specific advice on dosage see chapter 3. For full descriptions of all thirty-eight remedies and the states and personalities associated with them, see chapter 4. There is further advice on prescribing techniques in chapter 7. You are advised always to consult a qualified medical practitioner if you are in any doubt about your symptoms or otherwise worried about your health.

CHAPTER 7

HEALING OTHERS

Although the remedies are for everyone, there are times when it can be a comfort to get someone else's advice and help, especially when you feel you are still learning and you have your work cut out just to remember which remedy is which. You will almost certainly feel this way in the early days, and later on in this book you will find some information that will help you obtain further advice if you feel you need it.

This chapter will probably come in useful right away, however, because even if you feel barely qualified to help yourself you will find that as soon as other people learn about your interest in the flower remedies it is you who will be treated as the expert and asked to help decide which remedies they should be taking. Here we will give you a few pointers to help you respond effectively and constructively to these questions, whether you want to confine your help to the people you know well or to branch out, train to be a practitioner and run full-scale consultations.

PREPARATION

If you want to be able to help others with the remedies, the first thing you need to do is make a proper study of all thirty-eight remedies, and the emotional states that they are used to treat. Read the descriptions in chapter 4 thoroughly until you are able to remember with ease the different indications that you need to look out for when prescribing. Then turn to the other books available on the subject: the more you read the better prepared you will be, and the more likely it is that you will find the particular form of words that will help you recall a remedy without even trying.

Pay special attention to telling apart those remedies that at first sight can seem quite similar. For example aspen, cherry plum, mimulus, red chestnut and rock rose can all be described as remedies for fear – and were grouped together under that title by Dr Bach – but the type of fear in each case is very different. When you are faced with someone who says that he or she is afraid, you can't just jot down the first fear remedy that comes to mind, so you should take some time now to understand clearly the distinction between the red chestnut fear of what might happen to loved ones, the vague, unknown fear of the aspen type, the fear of madness and extreme actions felt by someone in the cherry plum state, and so on. And of course the same is true for all the other remedies that at first sight seem to be applicable to similar states. See chapter 8 for more help on this aspect of working with the remedies.

You might find that it helps you remember the different remedies – and gives you some practice at prescribing as well – if you sharpen your skills by finding type remedies for characters in your favourite soap opera, or well-known politicians, film stars, people in books, or your own friends and neighbours. What about the current prime minister, for example, or the president of the United States of America? Are they natural vine or elm types, as you might expect with people in such positions of great power and responsibility? Or do other type remedies seem to match their personalities more closely? And would you consider Charlie Chaplin's down-trodden little tramp a centaury person, always at the beck and call of others, or more of an agrimony type because he put a brave face on his poverty and loneliness?

This technique is great fun, but more importantly it is also a good way of familiarizing yourself with the kind of mental attitude you need if you are consistently to choose the right remedies on behalf of other people. It is used in the seminars held to train flower remedy counsellors and it can be an excellent confidence booster, not least because it allows you to get things wrong in private.

In addition to this you should be using the remedies in earnest to treat your own emotional crises and problems. As you decide on remedies, take them and observe their effects upon your own state of mind, so you will gain a more complete understanding of the way each remedy can help in different circumstances. This will stand you in good stead when you go on to help others in the same way. In time, as you get used to unravelling the symptoms you experience yourself to reach the real cause of a problem, you will be more able to do the same for others.

For fuller information on special techniques that can help you decide what remedies you need to take, see chapter 6.

CHOOSING REMEDIES FOR OTHER PEOPLE

Just as when you are selecting remedies for your own use, the key to helping others is the ability to get beyond the apparent symptoms in order to treat the underlying cause. This is especially true when you are treating people who may not perhaps know very much about flower remedies, since most people only turn to them when they are suffering from some physical disease, and they may not understand why an emotion or a state of mind is relevant to a case of flu, shingles or migraine.

By all means lend a sympathetic ear to the person's physical symptoms, but do not let this cloud the issue too much. Instead, encourage the person to open out more by asking simple questions. How does he feel about the illness? Does it seem to be associated with any particular moods or emotions? Is he facing any particular problems at home or at work that might be causing stress – and if so how is he reacting to this?

With those people who do not respond well to direct questions about their problems, you can get just as much information from general talk about work, friends and family, for although the illness is the occasion of the person's seeking help, the flower remedies are there to treat the whole person rather than a transitory physical condition. In any case you should try to make sure that the person you want to learn about does most of the talking.

As the person responds to your prompting, pay as much attention to the way he or she answers as you do to the replies themselves. Is she shy and timid, as if afraid to speak up? Or does she remain rather aloof and seem unwilling to discuss personal problems with you? In the first case, you might be dealing with a mimulus type; in the second water violet should be on your shortlist of remedies.

Pay attention too to any mannerisms that the person has. Impatiens people will often tap their feet and fidget in their chairs as if they can't wait to rush off somewhere else; clematis people on the other hand may drift off into space in the middle of a reply; while agrimony people will try to appear cheerful at all times and attempt to pass off every problem with a laugh.

As you note the replies, tone of voice and mannerisms of the person you are talking to you will find that a dozen or more remedies will quickly suggest themselves to you. The next stage is to decide on the few remedies that are really needed in this case. The general rule of thumb is that you should try to narrow the selection down to a maximum of six. In practice (and with practice) this is easy to do, and you should find that most of the people you see will not need more than two or three remedies.

You cannot overdose on the flower remedies, so there is no danger attached to giving too many different types in a single treatment bottle. However, too wide a mixture of remedies does tend to make the treatment as a whole less focused and hence less effective. If you feel that a case of fear demands the combined strength of aspen, mimulus, cherry plum and rock rose, then you almost certainly need to think a little more and probe a little deeper to identify the kind of fear you are treating – and, indeed, whether the fear is itself just a symptom of something else.

Having said this, if you are convinced on mature reflection that more than six remedies really are needed, then you should not hesitate to say so. If after a couple of weeks there is no improvement you can re-evaluate the situation then. And of course for those simple moods such as a temporary loss of enthusiasm for some task, or nervousness at the thought of attending a job interview, the correct remedies (in this case hornbeam and mimulus) can quickly be identified without the need for an in-depth interview.

RUNNING A CONSULTATION

Most people who use the remedies do so in a relaxed, simple way, advising friends and relatives about their everyday problems and never thinking of taking things any further. This is in fact the goal of the remedies and is the recommended way of approaching the whole subject: with the simple intention of helping yourself and others to a better way of life.

For those who are unsure how to go about helping others with the remedies, however, it can be useful to know a little about the way professional consultations are run. You do not need to be a professional to benefit from a professional approach, and as you will see the professional approach in this case is actually based entirely on common sense and care and concern for others.

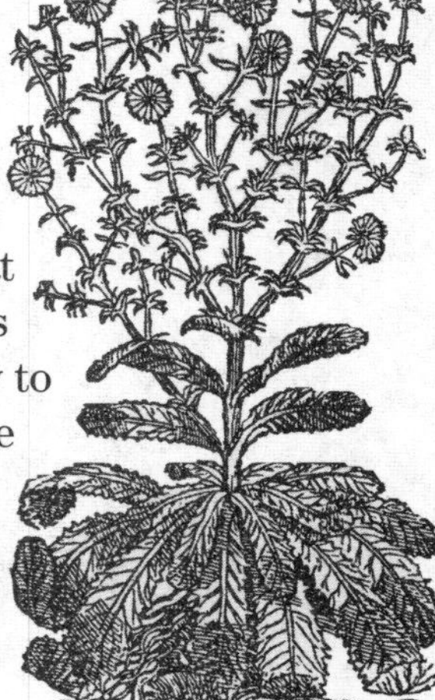

The first essential is to get to know the person you are treating. The only way of persuading people to behave naturally with you so that you can see what they are really like is to make them as relaxed as possible before the consultation starts – and the key to relaxing other people is to be relaxed yourself. Make sure you have five minutes to spare before the consultation starts so that you avoid starting in a rush. Practise a few opening remarks, so that even if you are a bag of nerves inside you still appear calm on the outside. And above all make sure you have prepared thoroughly by learning as much as possible about the remedies and how they are used. This will give you the confidence you need, and will allow you to concentrate on what the other person is saying instead of interrupting her every few moments to look up an indication in your trusty book.

At the very start of the consultation you might like to break the ice by offering a cup of tea or coffee, or by chatting about the weather, the person's journey to get to you, or any other general topic that occurs to you. Then you can ask a few easy, open questions – nothing that can be answered with just a 'yes' or 'no' – on topics that you think the person will enjoy talking about, whether sport, music, clothes or whatever. This is to open up the channels of communication and get the person used to responding to you and to talking about himself.

Of course, not everyone needs or wants to be led gently into the consultation proper, so when people ignore your carefully planned opening and launch at once into precise descriptions of emotional states and feelings, you should not attempt to hold them back.

If the person does not appear to know anything about the flower remedies you should make some effort to explain the basics, and in particular the fact that they work on the emotional/spiritual level and so do not attack physical disease directly. This is especially important with those who insist on discussing physical symptoms, since at some stage you have to leave the physical problems behind to get back to the underlying emotional causes. This can be difficult if the other person does not see the sense in making this move.

As the conversation proceeds and you learn more and more about the person you are talking to, you should be noting down anything she says or does that you think might be relevant to her character type or emotional state. In particular, jot down the remedies that you think will apply. Where a single symptom might indicate any one of several possible remedies, write them all down and then try to frame questions that you can ask later so as to narrow down the choice. For example, if someone is suffering from a lack of confidence you might write down

'confidence – larch or elm'. At a convenient break in the conversation – not immediately, since that might interrupt a fruitful train of thought – you could ask for information about the last crisis of confidence the person had, or ask how he copes when put in positions of authority. From such questions you should soon be able to decide whether larch is indicated for a general lack of self-confidence; or elm for the temporary lack of confidence in normally capable people; or even some other remedy, such as cerato, for those who lack confidence in their own judgement but, except when they have to make a decision, do not doubt their ability to do things.

Your questions don't have to be as direct as this if you don't want them to be. If you are faced with someone whose air of enthusiasm and high energy levels lead you to suspect a vervain type, a direct question would be to ask her if she feels strongly about politics – but you could also lead the talk around to nuclear testing or animal rights or any other topic of social concern in order to observe her reactions.

When you have decided on the remedy or remedies that you feel are indicated and you have listed them in your notes, it's a good idea to explain to the person being treated what each one is and why it is being given. This is not essential, since the remedies can be just as effective when the person doesn't know what is being taken, but it is desirable since it leaves the person feeling in control and able to play a conscious role in his own cure. But if you are going to run through the reasons for each of your decisions you must be prepared to justify them, especially if the emotional states you have diagnosed are not especially flattering. For this very reason, some counsellors choose not to always be too specific about the whys and wherefores, concentrating on dosage instructions and the treatment goal alone.

If only one or two remedies are needed, it is usually easiest to describe which stock remedies are required and to tell the person where to obtain them. (If none of your local shops stocks the remedies, there are a couple of addresses at the back of this book that might help.) If several remedies are involved, or the problem is a chronic (long-standing) one, you should make up a treatment bottle yourself, since the thought of doing this can be rather daunting for beginners. Tell the person how many drops to take and when – it's a good idea to write down the instructions as well, perhaps on a label that can be stuck onto the bottle.

F*ull details of dosages and the preparation of treatment bottles are given in chapter 3.*

Finally, don't throw away the notes you have made. Sometimes even the best of consultations ends with the wrong remedies being selected, so that after a couple of weeks you will hear that there has been no improvement. If this happens it is useful to have the notes from your original meeting to refer back to, and you will often find that on re-reading them you can spot some clue that brings the whole case into its correct focus. And where the consultation has been a complete success there is every likelihood that the person will be back on some future occasion, perhaps with an entirely different problem. If you have kept your notes you will have a head-start in terms of knowing her personality type and the kind of mannerisms and emotional states you need to look out for.

TAKING THINGS FURTHER

If you want to go beyond giving the occasional advice to friends and acquaintances, it is a good idea to consider further training. And you should certainly be thinking about this if you intend to offer a consultation service to the general public. In many parts of the world, people who want to set up as professional or semi-professional health counsellors have to have certain qualifications. Even where this is not the case, it can be difficult to obtain insurance cover if you do not possess a certificate to show that you have been properly trained in the service you are offering. You might think that you would not need to be insured, given that the flower remedies are so safe, and indeed I do not know of any case involving treatment with the remedies where an insurance policy has had to be called into play. But the fact remains that the damages that could be awarded following a prosecution for negligence or some other kind of compensation claim are potentially enormous. Balanced against this, the cost and inconvenience of doing things properly are insignificant.

There are flower remedy training centres in many countries throughout the world, and more are in the process of being set up. For further information on training courses and local availability, contact the Bach Centre – the address is at the back of this book.

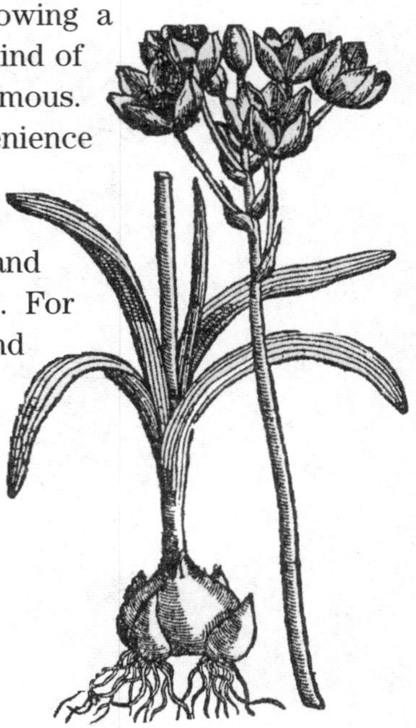

CHAPTER 8

Everyday Complaints

In this chapter we look at some of the common emotional problems and spiritual states with which the flower remedies can help you to deal.

There are no physical conditions mentioned in the list: as the remedies do not treat physical disease directly, it is not possible to provide a simple prescription guide along the lines of 'Take holly for a cold' or 'Where there is a fever, prescribe gentian'. Instead, whenever there are physical symptoms the task of the person prescribing the remedies is to get beneath the surface and find out what mental, emotional or spiritual state might lie behind the problem. Once this has been done and the correct remedies have been used to resolve any underlying personality conflicts, restoring the person to a state of emotional equilibrium, the body will be able to use its own natural powers of healing to combat the physical disease. In this sense only can the remedies be said to treat physical problems.

Where physical or any other symptoms persist or are severe you should always seek the advice of a qualified medical practitioner. Where emergency treatment is required it is especially important to remember that the remedies are best used in a complementary way, and that the most effective treatment in such cases is provided by orthodox Western medical techniques.
The safest rule is to always consult a doctor if you are in any doubt about the problem you are trying to solve.

When you have identified the emotional or other imbalances that need to be treated, it can be confusing to be faced with several different remedies that all appear to alleviate the same state, such as fear, depression or uncertainty. To help you select the specific remedy you require, the list of everyday feelings and mental states given here includes descriptions of the different remedies that would usually apply, along with the different aspects that are used to decide on the precise remedy required.

Remember that you often need to look beyond the obvious symptoms to find the real cause, and that the apparent mental state may be just another symptom of a deeper problem. For examples of how this can work, see the case histories in chapter 4, which also contains a full description of each of the thirty-eight remedies and should be referred to in conjunction with this chapter. For a detailed description of how to prescribe for yourself and others, see chapters 6 and 7. For full information on how to take the remedies and what the correct dosage is, see chapter 3.

ABSENT-MINDEDNESS

Clematis is the remedy for that absent-mindedness that arises when people are too busy dreaming of the future to pay attention to the present. Clematis people are day-dreamers, with a tendency to be drowsy and to drift off into their own worlds, even in the middle of a conversation.

For those who appear absent-minded because they are thinking too much of past regrets or past pleasures, honeysuckle is indicated. Both honeysuckle and clematis bring the mind back to the here and now so that the person can live an effective life and take action to overcome past problems, or to build in reality for the future.

Another state that could be described as absent-mindedness is the chestnut bud state. This is characterized by a failure to learn from past mistakes, which leads the sufferer to repeat actions that have already proved to be mistakes. Chestnut bud people take a long time to learn from their experiences and so find it hard to move on to new, perhaps more successful behaviour. The chestnut bud remedy helps the person to be more observant of what he is doing, so that he is able to profit from the mistakes not only of himself but of those around him too.

People in the white chestnut state may also appear absent-minded. This is because they are so preoccupied by repetitive, unwanted thoughts and worries that they forget to concentrate on where they are and what they should be doing. The absent-mindedness goes when the person is able to enjoy a calm mind, and so take notice once more of the real world.

ACCIDENTS

For accidents of all kinds the first thing to reach for is the Rescue Remedy, since this is specially formulated to deal with all the most common emotional states brought on by unexpected occurrences. For more information on the Rescue Remedy, see chapter 5.

Otherwise, and if the Rescue Remedy is not available, star of Bethlehem is the remedy to give to counteract the effects of shock. For terror, rock rose should be given. These two in conjunction or by themselves will help most people affected by an accident, and both are ingredients in the Rescue Remedy composite.

The remedies are not intended to replace normal medical care. With any accident, you should call for qualified medical assistance if you are in any doubt as to the seriousness of the injury. Do not move anyone who has been injured and cannot move unaided.

AGGRESSION

Where the aggression is externalized and accompanied by envy, hatred or suspicion of other people, holly is probably indicated. This helps the person to be more understanding and counteracts bad temper and negative emotions generally.

A different form of aggression is shown by those who ride roughshod over the feelings of others in an insensitive quest for power and authority. These are vine people. They do not hate others in the way the holly person does – rather they take it for granted that others will obey them, and use force without thinking when they do not get their own way. The vine remedy helps such people to be more considerate of others so that they can exercise wise leadership instead of heartless tyranny.

Often, however, the aggression is not itself a cause but only a symptom of some other underlying problem. Where this is the case, further investigation is necessary to pinpoint the correct remedy or remedies to use.

ALARM **see Shock**

AMBITION, LACK OF

For a complete lack of ambition where the person seems resigned to the present circumstances and makes no effort to change them, wild rose is the indicated remedy. People in this state seem weary and believe that there is nothing they can do but go on as they are, even when to others the possibilities for change seem ready to hand.

For those people who enjoy dreaming of great schemes, yet lack the ambition and drive necessary to put them into effect, clematis can be of help. The remedy aids such people to take a more realistic hold on life, to concentrate on what is achievable now instead of building castles in the air.

For the negativity and lack of ambition brought on by a discouraging setback of some kind, gentian can help to restore the desire and faith needed for success. Where the discouragement has grown into despair and hopelessness, so that it seems pointless to try to find a solution to one's problems, gorse may be given instead.

Finally there are those who are in fact very ambitious, who want to do something really worthwhile and who are often very capable people with a great deal to contribute. But they still seem to lack ambition because they drift from one occupation to another and are unable to make up their minds what their task in life really is. For such people, or for anyone who falls into this state from time to time, wild oat can help show the way ahead more clearly and so make it easier to choose the right direction.

APATHY

Wild rose is the most obvious remedy for those who are feeling apathetic and unenthusiastic about their lives. It is also used where people have given in to an illness without a struggle, resigning themselves to their condition as if they cannot be bothered to try to get well. The wild rose type tends to be something of a drifter and may complain of tiredness and a lack of vitality.

Where the apathetic indifference is caused by the person not paying sufficient mind to the present, other remedies might be indicated. For example, if the person is always day-dreaming and appears preoccupied, clematis is the natural first choice. If the apathy in the present is caused by a tendency to live in the past, then honeysuckle may be more appropriate.

Gentian would be indicated if the apathy was a symptom of the person's being discouraged following a setback of some kind, and for negative, melancholic thoughts generally.

APPRHENSION see FEAR

ARROGANCE see PRIDE

BULLYING see AGGRESSION; VIOLENCE.

COMPASSION, LACK OF

For those whose lack of compassion and sympathy is coupled with intolerance, so that they are critical and make no attempt to understand the problems other people have to cope with, beech is the remedy to select. The treatment aim is to introduce more compassion and understanding of others, so that the beech person is able to see the good in others as well as the things that are wrong.

In cases where the person is cruel and dictatorial rather than critical, vine may be selected. Vine people are strong, gifted leaders, but they can demand an unquestioning obedience that spares little time for the needs and problems of others. The remedy helps to soften the harder edges so that the vine person can guide instead of dominating, thus helping others to find their way in life more effectively.

For those who seem to lack compassion because they are too wrapped up in their own problems, heather might be chosen. This could be the case where the person talks constantly about her problems but is a poor listener when other people need to talk. But where an apparent lack of compassion is signalled by silence and withdrawal rather than perpetual talk, the person might be a water violet type. These people will offer advice and help if asked, but do not become personally involved, so they can appear aloof and disdainful. Water violet is given to help such people let down their guard so that their true compassion can shine forth.

COMPULSIVE BEHAVIOUR

Compulsive behaviour usually indicates that crab apple could be used to help rid the person of his or her unwanted obsessions. The type of behaviour that comes under this heading includes continual hand-washing, and checking and rechecking that the door is locked, the light switched off, the television unplugged and so on.

Crab apple can also be used where the behaviour is mental rather than physical – in other words, where it is unwanted thoughts rather than unwanted actions that cause trouble. For example, it might be given to someone who is obsessed with thoughts about disease or cleanliness, or fixated on a single subject or hobby horse. In some circumstances white chestnut may also be indicated. This is the remedy to calm unwanted worrying thoughts that continually return, preventing the person from concentrating on the things she should be doing. Agrimony might also be considered where the person suffering this condition has a tendency to present a cheerful face to the world in spite of her mental suffering, since her inability to relate her suffering to her everyday life could be the root of the problem. If necessary, of course, these different remedies can be combined – although with the help of the detailed remedy descriptions in chapter 4 you will usually be able to decide on only one of them.

Heather is the indicated remedy for another type of compulsive behaviour: the need to buttonhole people and tell them over and over again all about the most trivial problems and troubles. This can be exhausting for the people being talked to and can lead to the heather person suffering great loneliness as others start to avoid him. Again the remedy's ability to restore equilibrium to these people can be a great help and relief.

CRUELTY see Compassion, lack of; Violence.

DAY-DREAMING see Absent-mindedness.

DEPRESSION

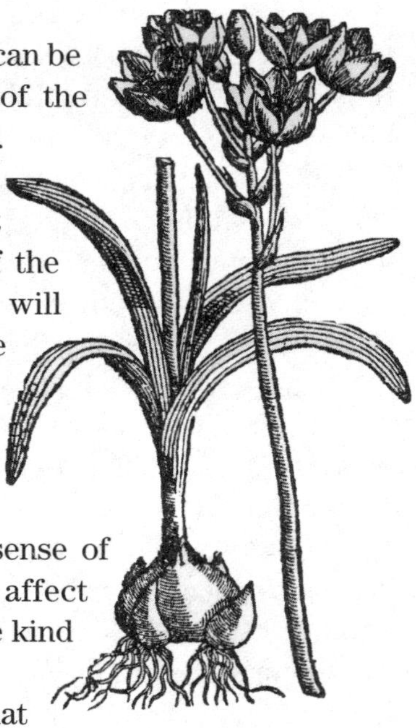

Finding the correct remedy for depression can be a problem for beginners, since so many of the remedies appear to deal with this condition. Here as always the key to successful prescribing is to get past the apparent symptoms and discover the real cause of the problem. Once this has been done, it will quickly become apparent which of the remedies is appropriate for the case in hand.

Perhaps the commonest type of 'true' depression you will encounter is the gentian state. This is the relatively mild sense of despondency and negativity that can affect anyone who has suffered a setback of some kind or who has had some bad news.

Mustard is for the deeper depression that makes the world look black and removes all joy from life. The key here is that the mustard state is always characterized by appearing unreasonable and without cause. Sufferers often say that they have no real reason to feel downcast, and that in fact their lives are full of things that should make them feel happy and contented. For people in this state, mustard can help to dispel the clouds so that the good things in life can be appreciated once more.

Where the depression is as strong as the mustard state but has been brought on by a known cause, gorse might be indicated. This is certainly the case if the person is feeling close to despair and is of the opinion that nothing can be done to help improve matters.

But in the vast majority of cases you will probably find that the depression itself is a symptom rather than a cause, and as such you will have to dig a little deeper to find the correct remedy. If the depression is caused by a lack of confidence, for example, you might choose larch. On the other hand, someone whose depression has been brought on because he has been unable to find his true vocation in life would probably benefit from wild oat, while the woman whose depression is caused by her inability to learn from her past mistakes will need chestnut bud. And the man whose depression springs from his self-pity and feelings of being hard done by will need willow. In all these cases the depression itself is not treated directly, but is attacked by means of the state of mind that is causing it.

DESPAIR

Like depression, despair comes in many shapes and sizes. For the despair that comes from a known cause, such as a serious illness, and where sufferers feel that nothing more can be done for them, gorse is generally indicated to restore the strength and faith needed to resume the struggle. At a further stage, when all possibilities of cure have been exhausted and there seems to be no other avenue to explore, sweet chestnut can help overcome the most terrible mental anguish. In cases of bereavement or any other event that causes this degree of despair, sweet chestnut is the natural first choice; but where the element of shock is felt to be a factor in causing the person to lose hope, star of Bethlehem may be given either instead of or in addition to one of the other remedies.

Just as it is used in cases of black depression that arise for no reason, so mustard is also used when there is despair without cause. It helps to restore stability in such cases and leave the person at peace with himself and with the world.

Other remedies that might be considered include pine, for the despair brought on by all-consuming guilt; crab apple, where feelings of self-hatred and self-disgust are at the root of the despair; and oak, where the person's tendency to go on working despite mounting tiredness has brought her close to collapse.

DISEASE see Illness.

DISSATISFACTION see Frustration.

EMERGENCIES see Accidents; Illness.

ENVY

Where envy is identified as one of the root causes of a person's misfortunes, holly is the first remedy that comes to mind. It is given in those cases where the envious thoughts have given rise to anger, usually externalized in the form of outbursts of temper, jealousy and other aggressive emotions.

Where the envious thoughts are kept inside, so that they fester into resentment – 'Why should she have so much when I have so little?' – then willow may be chosen. This is the remedy for those who begrudge the success of others and do nothing but criticize and carp. It helps people in this state to get things into perspective once more.

On the other hand, you may find some people who say that they envy the achievements of others but in fact do not seem to be envious at all – they say they are full of envy with a smile on their lips. This may indicate that the person is a larch type who is using praise of others as a way of covering a lack of self-confidence – the unspoken meaning is that the people praised can do something or other because they are so lucky or talented or rich, whereas the speaker is bound to fail and so need not bother to try. Larch is given in this case to help to remove the fear of failure that is the root of the problem.

FATIGUE

Where tiredness is the result of prolonged mental or physical effort, olive may be given to help to restore the person's strength. This applies, for instance, to someone who has been fighting a long battle against illness and now feels very weak and drained, just as it does to someone whose strength has been sapped by an emotional crisis.

Olive is often prescribed as a 'helper' remedy; in other words, one drawn on to assist a healing process initiated by other remedies. For example, if the fatigue is due to the person's having committed too much energy to a task or having taken on too many commitments, then vervain might be indicated. In cases where the person has gone plodding on with a job long after he should have stopped for a rest, oak is indicated. In both cases olive can be given in addition to these remedies to help restore strength more quickly.

There are other kinds of fatigue that do not have such obvious causes, however. Sometimes the fatigue comes at the mere thought of doing something, and we get into the Monday morning mood when tasks that we would normally undertake with pleasure seem beyond our strength. In cases like this hornbeam is the remedy to help restore the strength and courage needed to get on with life.

If the feeling that everything is too much effort continues for a long time, wild rose might be considered. This is the remedy for those who are too apathetic to get involved in life, whose fatigue is due to their lack of interest in and commitment to the world around them. In contrast to those in the hornbeam state, who generally find that once they have made the effort to get started their natural vitality comes back so that they enjoy the task, people in a wild rose state take little pleasure in anything at any stage and are resigned to their condition, doing little or nothing to change things.

Another possible remedy for dealing with fatigue and listlessness generally is clematis. This is for those people whose lack of interest in the present may leave them very drowsy and inclined to fall asleep at the drop of a hat – but these are not apathetic types as wild rose people are. Rather they are dreamers and love to lose themselves in grand schemes for the future.

As with all the states described here, the fatigue may of course be a symptom of another underlying problem. We have already seen how fatigue might be caused by overwork or too great a level of commitment to a task – but it could equally be the result of persistent worrying thoughts (white chestnut), or a feeling that one is overwhelmed by responsibility (elm), or the simple inability to say no to unreasonable demands (centaury). The rule of thumb is that in cases of fatigue you should always dig a little deeper, and you should never make the mistake of simply reaching for the olive every time.

FEAR

The commonest form of fear is probably the mimulus type. This is the simple fear brought on by a named cause, and includes the fear of giving a speech, the fear of spiders, birds or cats, and the fear of being made redundant or becoming ill. When anything in particular makes you feel afraid, mimulus can help to overcome the fear.

Mimulus is also used as a type remedy for those people who are of a timid and nervous disposition generally. People of the mimulus type will tend to be shy, especially in company, and will blush easily. They may even be afflicted with nervous conditions such as tics or stammering.

Where the fear is not of a known cause but rather comes over the sufferer for no apparent reason, aspen is the indicated remedy. The aspen fear also includes any vague foreboding that sometimes comes over us, such as the feeling that something unpleasant or terrible is about to happen.

Sometimes the aspen and mimulus fears may both be present, and in practice these two remedies are often given together where there seem to be elements of both types of fear. For example, the fear of spiders is certainly a mimulus fear since it is the fear of a known thing. But where the fear is exaggerated to an unreasonable degree so that it is felt the fear of spiders conceals some other, larger and unnamed fear, then aspen can be given as well. Similarly, the fear of the dark is again a named fear, but is often accompanied by all kinds of imaginary fears relating to the dreadful things that might be in the dark. To the extent that these fears can be described as uncanny, they become aspen fears.

The remedies are not intended to replace normal medical care. With any accident, you should call for qualified medical assistance if you are in any doubt as to the seriousness of the injury. Do not move anyone who is injured and cannot move unaided.

Both the mimulus and aspen fears can be very strong, but when they turn to real terror the correct remedy to choose is rock rose. This is the remedy that can help whenever true panic arises. At the scene of a serious *accident, for example, it can be used to treat the victims, those who have just missed being involved and even the witnesses. In such a situation rock rose would often be used in conjunction with star of Bethlehem to deal with the shock of the occurrence. For this very reason rock rose and star of Bethlehem are both included in the composite Rescue Remedy (see chapter 5).

Another common use for rock rose is to help deal with the extreme terror that can be brought on by a severe nightmare. It is especially useful when the person suffering the bad dream is a *child, since it is a quick and effective way to restore calm and dispel any lingering terror.

Always follow the treatment instructions in chapter 3, especially when giving the remedies to young children, since the undiluted stock bottles contain almost pure brandy.

Aspen, mimulus and rock rose are thus the three main remedies for most types of fear. But there are other flower remedies that can be of use in specific cases. Where the fear is of something happening to a loved one, such as the person falling ill or suffering an accident, red chestnut is indicated. For those extreme cases where the person fears that she may lose her sanity and do some *violence to herself or to those around her, cherry plum is the remedy to help her regain control of her thoughts and actions and turn her away from her suicidal or murderous thoughts. And where there is an exaggerated fear of dirt, disease and unclean things of all kinds, crab apple may help to rid the person of any feelings of self-disgust that may be the root cause of the fear.

> *Anyone who is talking about suicide or any other violent act should be taken seriously. Such people should seek the advice of a doctor, psychiatrist or other counsellor at the earliest opportunity.*

FORGETFULNESS see ABSENT-MINDEDNESS

FRUSTRATION

Impatiens people are especially inclined to suffer from frustration. They are always in a hurry and quickly become upset when others hold them back, so much so that they often end up doing the work of their subordinates just to speed things up. Some of them even take to finishing the sentences of slow talkers. The remedy helps such people to tolerate hold-ups without getting too worked up about things. Once they have been helped into a better frame of mind and have learnt to avoid being too hasty they often find that the old saying 'less haste, more speed' has an element of truth in it.

In many ways kindred spirits to impatiens types, the vervain person's frustration is also linked to

things not happening fast enough. These are people who are very committed to the causes they adopt. They have a great deal of nervous energy and throw themselves into each task they undertake, often overworking and taking on far too many things at once. The frustration can come where they are not making the progress they think they should be making, and is all the worse since they are highly strung perfectionists for whom only complete success will do.

The vervain remedy works to help such people to relax a little and realize that not everything can be achieved at once. Any tendency towards fanaticism is reduced as well, so that they can go about their activities in a more measured way and be more prepared to listen to the other side of any argument.

Scleranthus people too sometimes complain that they feel frustrated, but in this case the cause lies in their complete inability to make decisions. They change their minds too often to stick to one course for long, and the result can be wasted time and missed opportunities. While they are young this seems less important as there is time to make mistakes, but as they get older they can become downcast and frustrated by their lack of progress. The remedy is there to help them regain their balance so that they can take decisions calmly and with certitude – and stay on the path once they have chosen it.

A similar cause for frustration can exist with wild oat people, and with those for whom walnut would be indicated. Wild oat types do not suffer from indecision in everyday life as scleranthus people do, but when it comes to the really important things in life, such as choosing a career or forming relationships, they suddenly lose their way and cannot decide which direction to take. They try many different paths but never seem to hit on the right one. The situation is all the worse because wild oat types are often very talented individuals who want to do great things, and the continual frustration of their hopes leaves them bored and unhappy.

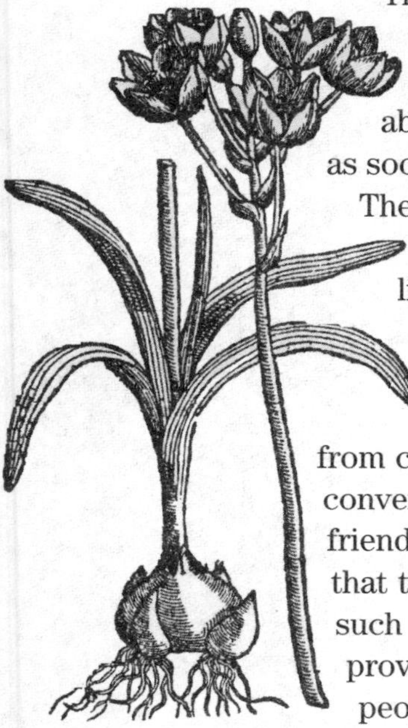

The remedy helps wild oat people to take stock of where their true talents lie so that they can define what ambitions they have and how to go about fulfilling them. Their frustration melts away as soon as this has been done.

The case of people in the walnut state is slightly different. These are people who in all likelihood know where they want to go and how they want to get there, but they are held back and their plans frustrated by adverse influences. What these influences are varies from case to case, but they may include other people, conventions, habits, links to the past, to family or to friends, or simply chance events that seem to suggest that the chosen way is not the correct one. Given in such cases, the link breaking walnut remedy helps provide the support, strength and determination that people need if they are to carry on with their plans in the teeth of all opposition and contrary circumstance.

GREED

Perhaps the remedy most associated with greed is chicory. People in a chicory state are selfish and possessive, wanting to control others and keep themselves at the centre of all love and attention. They treat their loved ones like possessions, almost as if they see little difference between human beings and other goods and chattels. In the pursuit of the ideal of possession they show themselves to be resourceful, deceitful and manipulative, and never give anything to anyone without an ulterior motive. The chicory remedy is given to help such people enjoy real human relationships again, freely offered and accepted: a greater thing by far than simple ownership.

Hatred, envy and aggression are the signs of the holly person, and it is quite common to find these negative emotions associated with greed of one kind or another. These are people who lack love and tolerance and who vent their vexations on others, but far from bringing relief this leads to nothing but discomfort, for the holly person often suffers great mental or emotional pain even when there is no obvious physical reason for it. The remedy is given to help such people share themselves and their love with others, and to encourage them to think with a more open and generous mind.

The greed of vine people is very specific: what they want is power and authority. With them thought is next to action, so they do not covet these things in quiet but rather go out and seize them, brushing aside anyone who dares stand in their way. The vine remedy is used to wash away the negative side of the vine character so that the positive side – that of a generous, decisive guide – can shine forth.

GUILT

Sometimes there is a good reason for guilty feelings – a bad act committed in the past, for example. At other times we may blame ourselves for things over which we have had no real control. We may even feel guilty when other people who should take the blame seem not to give their actions a second thought. At this point one can start to talk of a full-scale guilt complex which can, if unchecked, make the sufferer's life a complete misery.

In all these cases the pine flower remedy is indicated to help the person come to terms with any past misdeeds and see the faults of others in their proper light, instead of taking responsibility for them.

Where the state is one of simple regret for things that happened in the past, you might also consider honeysuckle. This is called for where such regrets have

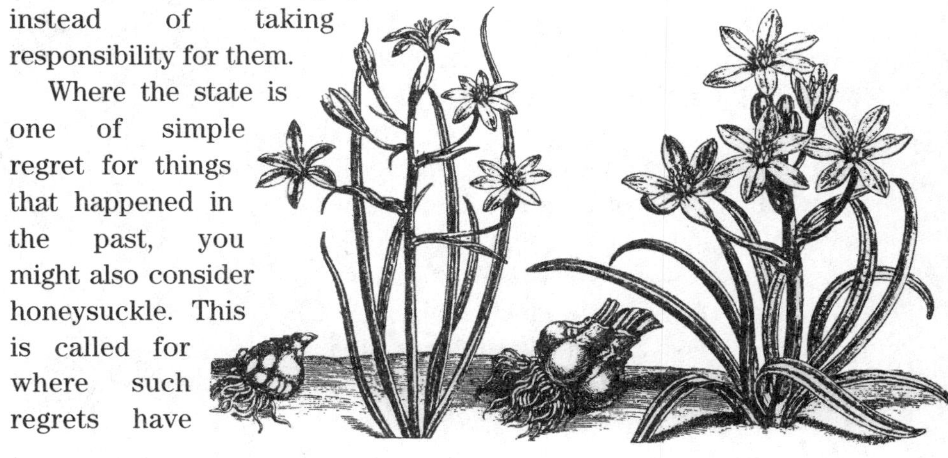

caused the person to withdraw from the present in order to live more fully in the past.

White chestnut can also help in those cases where guilty thoughts run round and round in the head, leaving the sufferer powerless to call a halt to them. The white chestnut state is often accompanied by sleeplessness and a lack of concentration, caused by the fact that the person's attention is held by the unwanted thoughts.

HOMESICKNESS see NOSTALGIA.

HOSTILITY see AGGRESSION.

HYPOCHONDRIA

Hypochondria can of course be a symptom of any number of mental and emotional problems, and as such the flower remedies indicated will vary from person to person. Nevertheless, some types of people and some specific emotional states are particularly prone to hypochondria, and they are the ones listed here.

Where there is some small medical condition that has grown in the person's mind to the point where it seems to dominate everything else, crab apple can be given. This is the remedy to wash away feelings of being unclean or contaminated and so help the person regain control of her thoughts.

Heather types are also preoccupied with minor ailments and talk about them incessantly to other people, to the point where their hapless listeners can start trying to avoid them. The heather remedy is given in such cases to help turn the person's attention out from the self and towards other people and the wider world.

When talking about their various illnesses, heather types sometimes become tearful and may exaggerate deliberately to invoke the sympathy of their audience. This is a trait they share with chicory types, although the latter are far more manipulative and domineering than the rather downtrodden heathers. Chicory people are more like generals waging total war in order to gain a single objective, which can be summed up as complete control over and possession of their loved ones. To this end they are not above deliberate deceit, and the 'illnesses' they suffer from may be carefully faked to give them a hold over others. The chicory remedy is used to help people in this state let go of loved ones so that love once more comes to mean care for others rather than control over them.

Willow people are those who seem to take a positive – although gloomy – delight in being ill, so much so that when they are getting better they are the last to admit it. Sulky and born complainers, they make bad patients since nothing that is done ever pleases them, and it is their perverse pleasure to compare their own wretchedness with the undeserved good health of other people, even when the lucky others are in fact coping with far more serious health problems with much less fuss.

The willow remedy helps turn negative thoughts into positive ones, allowing the willow person to see his problems in perspective and take pleasure in the good things in life instead of wallowing in the bad.

Lastly, people in a wild rose state of apathy and resignation can easily start to believe that their often minor problems are in fact incurable diseases, perhaps even inherited conditions, and that as such nothing can be done to help them. The indicated remedy helps to wash away such feelings so that the sufferer can see things in a more rational light and take the necessary steps to obtain a cure.

ILLNESS

The flower remedies are not intended to replace normal medical care. For any illness other than a minor ailment, you should always consult a qualified medical practitioner.

In any case of sudden *illness where there is shock and great fear both in the sick person and in family and friends, Rescue Remedy can be given at once to allow the situation to be faced calmly and let the body's natural healing functions come into play as soon as possible. For more information on Rescue Remedy, see chapter 5.

Each of the remedies that together make up the Rescue Remedy can also be usefully given by itself, according to how the person responds to the illness. Where the main emotion felt is shock at the bad news, star of Bethlehem is called for. For cases where the primary feeling is one of great fear and panic, rock rose is the indicated remedy. If the news has brought a loss of control and hysteria or the threat of the same, cherry plum helps restore rationality so that the situation can be faced in a reasoned manner. For any feelings that the affected person (or anyone else) might be about to faint, clematis may be given, while impatiens helps to ease the terrible mental agitation caused in such cases.

For illnesses that come on more gradually or which have been known about for some time, any of the remedies can be called on, depending on the individual's present state of mind, and of course the type of person he or she normally is.

Two remedies might be singled out in this connection, however, because of the way they are often called on to help all kinds of people suffering from all kinds of disease. They are crab apple and gentian, and both are used as 'helper' remedies – in other words, given in addition to a main treatment made up of type and mood remedies.

Crab apple is used to counteract feelings of uncleanness and contamination, whether mental or physical. It may be taken internally in the usual way, or used as an external cleanser where a particular area of the body is affected.

Gentian is widely used to help those who are feeling despondent and downhearted following a setback in a course of treatment – whether treatment with the remedies or by any other means. It helps counteract the temporary loss of faith which, if left untreated, might itself harm the person's health still more and turn eventually to true despair. Where things have already got this far gorse is indicated instead of gentian, as this is the remedy for those who believe that nothing more can be done for them.

IMPATIENCE see IRRITABILITY

INADEQUACY

For the temporary feeling of inadequacy that can overcome normally confident, capable people, elm is the indicated remedy. The elm state strikes when responsibilities and pressures mount up to such an extent that the person feels she can no longer cope with them. The remedy helps restore self-confidence and remove all such doubts.

Whereas the elm person is a normally adequate type, larch people feel inadequate most of the time because of their lack of self-confidence. They are so convinced that they will fail that they do not even bother trying to do things, even when they feel in their hearts that they do have some ability. For this form of inadequacy – more imagined than real – larch is the remedy to choose.

Where the inadequacy is real – that is to say the person really does seem to lack will-power and is incapable of standing up for himself – then centaury is indicated. This is certainly the case with a timid character who is under the sway of other more dominant types.

INDECISIVENESS

The obvious first choice for those who suffer from indecisiveness is scleranthus. This is indicated when the person is unable to make up his or her mind about the smallest trifles, as well as important matters. The mind seems to hop constantly from one alternative to the next in this state, and people seem unable to maintain the same ideas or direction from one moment to the other. Consequently they can appear weak-willed and unreliable – not because they are dishonest, but because they change their minds from one moment to the next.

Where normally decisive people suffer from the inability to make really important decisions, but are still able to decide on the small things in life, scleranthus is probably not indicated. Instead, wild oat can be given where the problem concerns which path in life the individual should take, or cerato where the person seems to know what she wants to do but lacks faith in her judgement and so seems indecisive, since she unnecessarily asks all and sundry for their advice.

INSOMNIA

Sleeplessness can be caused by any number of mental states, and as such almost all the remedies might be used to treat different cases. Nevertheless, there are a few remedies that have become particularly associated with insomnia because the mental states they counteract so often lead to loss of sleep.

Where the insomnia is caused by persistent worrying thoughts that seem to plague the mind, white chestnut might help. This is the remedy to use when repetitive thoughts of all kinds trouble the mind, a situation which almost always disturbs or prevents sleep.

A similar problem is where the person has put a brave face on problems during the day but finds that at night the churning mental torture returns, again resulting in an inability to sleep. For this state agrimony is indicated.

Sometimes the tension experienced during the day may lead to an inability to unwind and relax, and hence to insomnia. Impatiens people often feel frustrated at the slowness of others, which can lead to this kind of mental tension. Rock water people also tend to be tense because of their mental rigidity, and vervain types too find that their extreme mental energy and fanaticism can leave them unable to relax. The type remedy in each case should help to remove the cause of any sleeplessness.

Where a severe nightmare has woken you up, rock rose is the remedy to restore calm quickly and let you get back to sleep. Where the dream itself is forgotten immediately after waking but a vague feeling of terror or apprehension persists which leaves the person wakeful and afraid of going back to sleep, then aspen is indicated.

In all cases where the person is physically tired as a result of being unable to sleep, olive can be given to strengthen the mind and body – but this is not a long-term solution. Only by regaining a proper mental and emotional balance can the person hope to overcome the problem once and for all.

INTOLERANCE

For those people who lack tolerance when it comes to the lives of others, beech is the indicated remedy. People of this type never try to understand other people's problems and ideals; they are quick to criticise and complain about even the smallest habits and customs that others adopt.

Impatiens might be called for where the intolerance is directed specifically at people who are slow of thought or action. The impatiens type is someone who tends to be full of nervous energy and wants to get things done quickly, which can lead to frustration and great mental tension.

Where an apparently high set of values and intolerance of those who do not meet them seems to be more a question of gaining control over loved ones, the person may be a chicory type. Tell-tale signs to watch out for include overinterference in the lives of others and a need for constant attention.

Finally, for those people whose lack of tolerance is directed at themselves, in that they set themselves high, rigid standards which lead to self-denial and repression, rock water is the indicated remedy.

IRRITABILITY

Impatiens is the remedy for those very quick people who become irritated when things do not happen as fast as they would like. Fast workers and thinkers themselves, they become very frustrated when they are unable to speed things up enough. Impatiens can help to make these people more tolerant of those who are slower than they are.

Where the irritation is caused by the habits and mannerisms of other people, with a reaction often out of all proportion to the apparent cause, the person might benefit from beech, which is the remedy for this form of intolerance.

Irritable people who are also selfish, manipulative and possessive in their personal relationships may need chicory. In this case the irritability may be felt when the person feels that loved ones are not living up to some ideal, or that she is not getting the attention and gratitude she deserves from those around her.

Where irritability shades into real anger or even hatred, holly might be indicated. This is so where the emotions are externalized – but where the irritation takes the form of resentment, bitterness and a continual grumbling about others, willow should be the preferred choice.

JEALOUSY see ENVY

LISTLESSNESS see APATHY; FATIGUE

LONELINESS

Many of the emotional states and characteristics that the flower remedies deal with can lead to the person's feeling lonely. So while there is no remedy for loneliness as such, the remedies can help to deal with the cause of the loneliness and in this way make it easier for sufferers to get back in touch with other people.

For those who tend to hold themselves aloof from others and so appear condescending and proud, water violet is indicated to help break down the barrier they have allowed to build up between themselves and the rest of humanity. Water violet people will still like their own company, of course, but when they want companionship they should find it more easily.

People who prefer to get on with things by themselves because they find other people too slow can on occasion suffer from loneliness as well. Impatiens is the remedy to help such people be more tolerant and understanding of other people's ways of living, and also help them slow down enough to make friends.

Some types are more scared of loneliness than others. Whereas water violet and impatiens people will find that loneliness creeps up on them unexpectedly, heather people suffer from the fear of loneliness as well as from loneliness itself. This is why they are so determined to avoid it, cornering other people and talking at them non-stop to prevent them from getting away. This behaviour may work for a time, but soon people begin to avoid heather types so that in the long run the constant attempt to keep hold of an audience is counterproductive. The heather flower remedy helps such people to start listening to others instead of always talking at them, so that a normal human interaction is once again possible.

Rather than being scared of loneliness, agrimony types simply fear being left by themselves. This is because they are able to cover up their problems when they are in company, since they can play the joker and generally act as if nothing at all is wrong. But when they are by themselves they find that their churning thoughts come back. Agrimony is the remedy to help such people get their lives back into balance, so that they can face up to and deal with their problems instead of running away from them.

Other people react to a fear of loneliness by attempting to control the lives of loved ones. This is the chicory state. For example, the chicory remedy can help the mother who tries to keep her grown-up children on a leash, insists that they visit her every weekend, and gets upset and jealous if anyone or anything prevents them from doing so. The aim of the remedy is to turn the self-regarding, possessive love into a more open love that really is directed towards the good of others. The fear of loneliness in this case – again often a self-fulfilling prophecy – will go once the person finds she is truly appreciated and loved for herself and for what she can give to others.

MELANCHOLIA

For the melancholy that comes for no apparent reason, mustard is the remedy. The mustard state is one that is particularly common with adolescents, whose bouts of causeless gloom are well known.

Where the melancholy has been brought on by a discouraging piece of news that has caused the person to lose faith in what he is doing, then gentian is an appropriate remedy to give. For more severe cases where the melancholic thoughts are beginning to turn to despair and hopelessness, gorse may be given instead.

MISERY see DESPAIR

MOODINESS

For those who swing constantly from one mood to another, being happy one moment and sad the next and never seeming to settle for long in one state of mind, scleranthus may be indicated. This is the remedy for those whose lack of balance leaves them in a state of complete indecision and uncertainty. It helps them to exchange their wavering for a calm certainty that equips them to deal with the ups and downs of life.

Where moodiness translates as an apparently motiveless gloom, mustard may help. The mustard state is unlike other forms of depression in that it comes for no apparent reason – but for all this it can be intense and cause great suffering to those it afflicts. The remedy in this case restores stability and peace and lifts the clouds of depression.

A different, although often equally unjustified moodiness is that betrayed by those people whose feelings of guilt and self-blame nip all pleasure in the bud. They appear downcast and miserable when there seems no reason to be this way; hence they can appear sullen. Pine is the indicated remedy for this condition: the sufferer will gain a more balanced attitude towards the idea of responsibility, and even when there are good reasons to feel guilty the poison of guilt will not be allowed to destroy the person's whole life.

Finally, willow people can also appear sulky and sullen, seeming actually to enjoy spreading gloom all around them. They are irritable and full of self-pity; but the remedy helps to counteract this negativity so that the sufferer can take a more positive view of life.

NERVOUS TENSION see STRESS.

NIGHTMARES

For the terror caused by severe nightmares, rock rose is the first remedy to turn to. This can quickly help restore calm, so that the person can go back to sleep without fear.

The Rescue Remedy (see chapter 5) is often used in this situation as well, simply because the flower remedy 'first aid kit' is more likely to be ready to hand at the moment of waking. As well as containing rock rose, Rescue Remedy is formulated with cherry plum, the remedy for any loss of mental or emotional control. This can be a great help where the nightmare has led to uncontrollable panic or hysteria.

Vague terrors that persist after a nightmare has ended and been forgotten, together with all uncanny fears of the dark and so on, can be further helped by aspen.

NOSTALGIA

Nostalgia is usually thought of as a problem confined largely to older people. But in fact anyone who looks back too much to some golden past, however recent it might be, is failing to live fully in the present. That includes the child in autumn who thinks of nothing but the summer holidays, as surely as the eighty-year-old reliving her pre-war youth.

When nostalgia and living in the past cause people to lose interest in the present, honeysuckle is the remedy to help keep memories in check so that the person can move on through the present, full of hope, free of any fear of the future or doubts about tomorrow.

Nostalgia can also be an element in hindering someone from taking a step forward in life. For such unwanted ties to the past, and for any other circumstances that might hinder a progression, walnut is indicated. Walnut is the link-breaker, lending strength to those going through a major change in life or trying to take an important decision, and can be usefully prescribed for any of life's milestones, including birth, teething, puberty, menopause and bereavement.

OBSESSIONS see COMPULSIVE BEHAVIOUR

PANIC

Panic is an extreme, acute problem, and the first cure to hand is usually the composite Rescue Remedy (see chapter 5). The relevant remedies within the composite are rock rose, which is the specific remedy for terror and panic, and cherry plum, which helps the loss of self-control and hysteria that often accompany panic.

Of course, either of these flower remedies can also be given alone or in conjunction with others. Both of them are usually given as remedies for temporary states rather than as type remedies, but this does not mean that they cannot be used for chronic (long-standing) problems as well. For example, someone suffering from a severe long-term phobia that causes real panic can benefit from rock rose, although a less serious fear probably indicates mimulus, or on occasion aspen. There are also those who are prone to the cherry plum state and have a tendency to lose control of themselves. The loss of control in such cases can take the form of panic, or manifest itself in unreasonable anger or even bouts of physical violence.

For those attacks of near-panic that arise for no apparent reason, as if out of a clear blue sky, aspen rather than rock rose is the first choice. Aspen fears include fear of the unknown, of what will happen after death, and superstitious, irrational, uncanny fears; all of which can turn to genuine panic if they are not faced and overcome early enough.

POSSESSIVENESS see GREED; SELFISHNESS

PRIDE

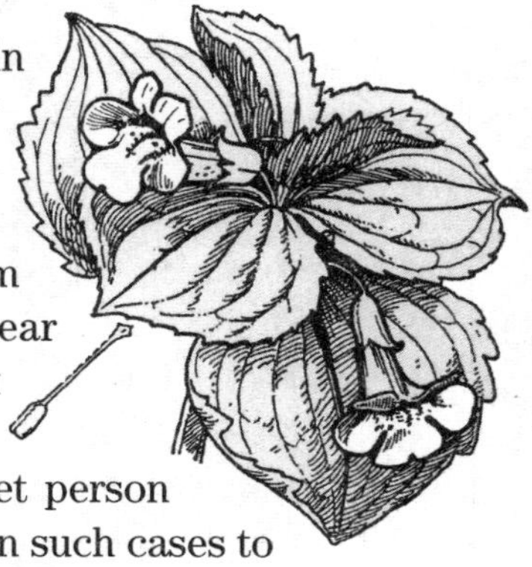

The pride that water violet people feel in themselves is usually merited, in that they tend to be clever, capable and calm in any situation and are fully aware of their abilities. But their tendency to stand a little apart from other people can make them appear condescending and aloof. Other people think they are being patronised and so in time a barrier can grow up between the water violet person and the rest of humanity. The remedy is used in such cases to soften any tendency to be too proud, adding a measure of sympathy and interest in others. This helps to break down the barriers so that the water violet can continue to enjoy his own company without the worry that this might be the only company he will ever enjoy.

Like water violet people, those of the vine type are often right to be proud of their abilities and achievements, since they are born leaders who are capable of great things. When the negative side of their characters is emphasized, however, they can be overbearing. At such times their pride becomes aggressive, leading them to ignore the legitimate needs and concerns of others in a ruthless drive to dominate. The remedy helps to remove any tendencies of this type, so that the vine person can demonstrate an interest in others for their own sakes rather than seeing them as tools to be used for her own ends.

The pride of people in the beech state is rather less grand, since it manifests itself in continual criticism of others and a lack of tolerance for anyone who fails to meet the beech person's standards. The remedy is given to counteract the tendency to judge others by often inapplicable criteria. It also helps the beech person to look with a little more humility at the everyday heroism of people less fortunate than he is.

Spiritual pride is the sin of the rock rose type. These are people who are concerned above all with perfecting themselves. In the effort to achieve their goals they are prepared to suffer and go to any extreme, thinking nothing of the most rigorous exercise or diet regimes and sometimes taking self-denial to the brink of martyrdom. And while they are not hard on others – they aren't interested enough in other people for this – they nevertheless tend to look down on them and are absolutely convinced of the rightness of their pet theories and the wrongness of every other way of life. Their spiritual isolation can leave rock water people lonely, and their puritan streak too often leads to a life empty of simple pleasures. The remedy's task is not to weaken the high ideals that mean so much to them, but simply to leave them more receptive to other people and other ideas. By leading them gently away from fanaticism, the remedy opens them up to a different and more human form of spirituality.

REMORSE see Guilt

RESENTMENT

The remedy for resentful thoughts is willow. People in the willow state brood on how unlucky they have been and believe that only they have suffered, while other people all seem to have lots of luck – and undeserved luck at that. Sulky and full of self-pity, they begrudge the success and happiness of others and moan and complain constantly. The willow flower remedy helps people in this emotional state to come out of their introspective bitterness so that they no longer look at the negative side of everything.

It's easy to caricature this state, and in some ways it is quite a healthy reaction to laugh about those who grumble all the time – but for those living through a willow state life can be a trial, devoid of all pleasure, so their problems should always be taken seriously. All the more so since everyone enters into the willow state from time to time.

Sometimes chicory people can appear to be full of resentment too. But often this apparent resentment is a mask for simple jealousy, and the successes and luck complained of would be accepted if only the beneficiary would give more attention to the possessive chicory.

When silent, sulky resentment gives way to open envy and ill will, holly may be preferred to willow. Holly is the remedy for those kinds of negative, aggressive emotions that are the antithesis of love and good fellowship, and which are externalized in outbursts of anger and hatred. Where willow smoulders, holly flames.

SELF-DISGUST

The first remedy to consider for people who feel disgust and dislike for themselves or their appearance is crab apple. People in the crab apple state can feel unclean either physically, as for instance where there is some unpleasant or disfiguring disease with which they have to cope; or mentally, for example if they have done or said something of which they feel ashamed. Crab apple washes away any sense of dirtiness and uncleanness and lets the person see things in a more balanced way.

As always, however, there may be other states of mind that can be described as self-disgust, but for which other remedies are more appropriate. Larch people, for example, lack confidence and can feel inferior to others; pine types torment themselves with guilt and demand far too much of themselves; rock water puritans can condemn themselves for their own inability to live up to the high standards they set; and people in a wild oat state can find that their uncertainty as to which path to take in life leaves them dissatisfied and depressed. All these people may say that they are disgusted at themselves – but a little thought will show that crab apple would not be the first choice for any of them, since any self-disgust in their cases is a symptom rather than a cause.

SELFISHNESS

Chicory is the first remedy to consider when selfishness seems to be the cause of a person's problems. The negative chicory state is one in which love for others has been perverted into possessiveness, so that an emotion which should flow out to others is directed back at the self. Chicory people demand constant attention from those close to them, and are forever interfering and offering unwanted help and advice so as to bind other people more closely to them. When they don't get their own way they quickly become upset and complain that they are not appreciated.

The remedy works to overcome the negative aspects of the chicory state and replace them with the positive ones: selflessness in place of selfishness and a desire to help others without expecting anything in return.

Beech and heather people too might appear selfish, in that they do not consider the problems of others. But in both cases selfishness is not really an accurate description. With the beech person, thoughtless criticism of other people's failure to live up to set standards is better described as intolerance; while the heather remedy is used for those who are too wrapped up in their own troubles to listen to those of others. Their lack of interest in others is not designed to win them any advantage, so that they are not so much selfish as self-centred.

Vine people can also appear selfish, and with rather more justification. But unlike the chicory person who manipulates others through emotional blackmail, selfishness of the vine variety manifests itself through the open assumption of authority over others. Vine people take for granted the absolute obedience of other people and can show a cavalier lack of concern for their welfare. The remedy helps vine types to realize their potential as leaders but takes away the drive for domination – and of course all charges of selfishness fade away once this is achieved.

SENSITIVITY

For those whose oversensitivity to outside influences and moods sometimes gets in the way of what they want to achieve in life, walnut is the indicated remedy. People in the walnut state might find that a forceful personality or an idea forcefully stated can cause them to waste precious time or even abandon courses of action that they know to be right. At other times it is some link to the past or an old way of doing things that gets in the way. In either case walnut helps to protect those susceptible to such influences so that they can go on to do the things they want, regardless of the opinions of others and in the teeth of every adverse circumstance.

Susceptibility of a different kind is counteracted with the aspen flower remedy. This is for those who find that they are sensitive above all to vague forebodings and unspecified fears, such as those felt in certain empty houses or anywhere where there has been a tragedy in the past. These feelings can strike anyone, of course, and the remedy is called for in all such cases – but those who are true aspen types will be especially sensitive to the atmosphere around them, and for them the aspen remedy will prove invaluable, helping to calm fears and turn the soul towards the bright light of life.

Other kinds of sensitivity include that betrayed by the mimulus type, who finds social events a great trial because of his shyness and is very prone to blushing and stammering, especially when called on to take a leading role of any kind. For such people mimulus is the indicated remedy to lend them the

courage and give them the confidence they need to play their full role in life, free of fear and full of good humour. Centaury people, on the other hand, have a genuine and deep concern for the welfare of others but can find that other people take advantage of their sensitive natures to control or manipulate them. The remedy gives them the strength to say no to unreasonable demands. And the complaining willow type is in fact suffering from a form of sensitivity, although in her case it is criticism which she feels too keenly. If she had a more robust sense of her own worth she perhaps would not feel so bitter about being slighted – and for this reason part of the role of the willow remedy is to encourage a reasonable pride in who and what she is.

SHAME see GUILT

SHOCK

The remedy for any kind of shock, whether caused by an accident, sudden bad news or a fright, is star of Bethlehem. This flower remedy works to calm the sufferer and restore the normal mental and emotional equilibrium, so that whatever caused the shock can be faced up to and dealt with in a rational manner.

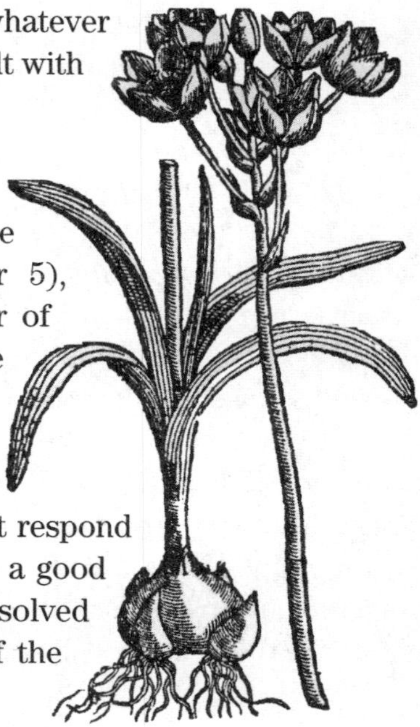

Because shock by definition comes suddenly and unexpectedly, star of Bethlehem finds a natural place in the composite Rescue Remedy (see chapter 5), where it is at hand when needed. But star of Bethlehem is also called for where the effects of the shock do not manifest themselves for months or even years after the event. Indeed, many flower remedy counsellors advise that where people do not respond to the remedies selected for them it can be a good idea to ask whether there might be any unresolved shock in the past that could be the root of the current problem.

SHYNESS see Timidity

SICKNESS see Illness

SLEEPLESSNESS see Insomnia

STRESS

Stress is a catch-all term for a number of related conditions, and the causes vary from person to person. As such it should be no surprise to learn that any one of the remedies might be used to help a person complaining of stress, and that before any of them is prescribed the underlying causes of the stress should be identified.

That said, some types of people and some emotional states are particularly associated with stress, and these are listed here.

Agrimony is for those people who suffer from stress in the form of mental torture: churning thoughts which return whenever they are left alone and which they sometimes try to quiet with drink or drugs. Agrimony people always try to hide their problems, presenting a smiling face to the world so successfully that it often comes as a surprise to their friends and relatives to learn that they have any problems at all. The remedy helps such people to come to terms with their troubles and so master the things that make them feel stressed instead of trying to run away from them.

Elm and oak people sometimes find that their ability to cope with responsibility can itself lead them into stressful situations, since it is all too easy for them to take on too much. When this happens to elm people they can feel suddenly overwhelmed by all the things they have agreed to do and so come to doubt their usually undoubted ability. Oak people, on the other hand, will simply plod on and on and try even harder, with the result that when the breakdown does come it is all the worse. The elm and oak remedies help these different cases to take up the reins again with renewed confidence and strength.

Vervain types are rather different, but here too there is a tendency to overwork: 'Tried to do too much' could be the epitaph on many a vervain headstone. These people are enthusiasts who know no half measure in their commitment to the things they undertake. While this is an admirable quality, stress is an obvious danger that they do little or nothing to avoid. Indeed, they become so worked up about things that they can find it impossible to relax – and it is at this stage that the remedy can help to get things back into balance and allow the vervain person to step back and take stock every once in a while, instead of always rushing on to the next task.

Impatiens people are also inclined to suffer from mental and physical tension. They are forever on the move, impatient to see things finished and irritable with anyone who does not move fast enough for their liking. The constant, largely self-imposed time pressures that they live under, coupled with a tendency to become irritated and frustrated at the least delay, make them prime candidates for stress-related problems of all kinds. Fortunately the remedy can help them to slow down a little and become more patient and less hasty. This in turn allows them to relax.

Other remedies that may be particularly associated with stress include pine, for those who are never content with what they have done and blame themselves unnecessarily when things go wrong; rock water, for those whose tendency to self-denial and rigidity of mind leaves them tense and unable to be kind to themselves; and white chestnut, for times when mental exertion makes it hard to switch off at the end of the day and leaves unwanted thoughts circling around the brain. Indeed, wherever stress leads to the constant re-running in the mind of the day's events or to continual worrying, white chestnut can be a useful helper remedy to choose.

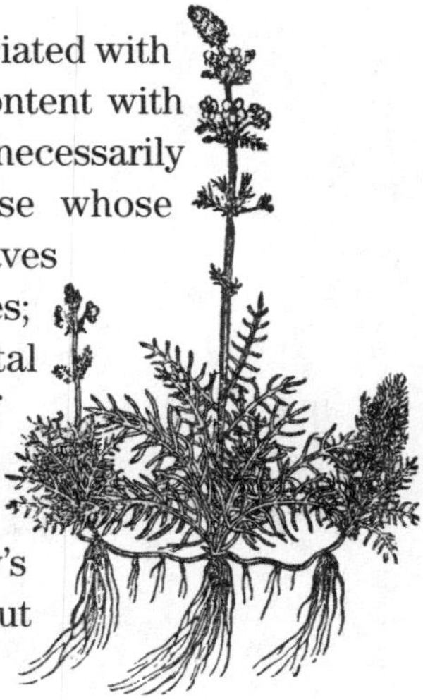

TENSION see Stress

TIMIDITY

For those who tend to be timid and shy, who blush easily or who stammer and become tongue-tied in company, mimulus is the indicated remedy. It allows such people to feel more in control of their emotions and the situations they encounter, helping to lend them the courage and confidence they need in order to face the world without flinching.

Where the person is not so much shy as unable to stand up for him or herself, then centaury should be considered instead of mimulus. Centaury is the remedy for people who allow others to impose upon them and who find it next to impossible to say no to any favour, request or order. The remedy allows such people to cast off the chains forged by other people's desires, so that they can offer or refuse service freely and as an equal.

TIREDNESS see Fatigue

UNHAPPINESS see Melancholia

VANITY see Pride

VIOLENCE

For those who fear that they will lose control of themselves, lose their sanity and *do harm to themselves or to others, cherry plum is the indicated remedy. People in this state, if not helped, can find themselves

Anyone who is talking about suicide or any other violent act should be taken seriously. Such people should seek the advice of a doctor, psychiatrist or other counsellor at the earliest convenience.

the victim of violent rages in which they do and say things that would normally horrify them. In extreme cases they may attack someone, or even consider suicide. Cherry plum is the remedy to calm such states of mind and give the individual control over her emotions once more. Holly is for those who are not so much threatened by a loss of control, as people in the cherry plum state are, as full of hatred towards others. The anger they feel, although it is often unmerited, is more controlled and sustained than the violent impulses of the cherry plum; but it is no safer, because if it does spill over into violence the result can be just as bad. The remedy in this case works to wash away hatred and replace it with understanding and tolerance.

Of course in many other cases violence – whether actual or potential – is a symptom rather than a cause, so that the remedy used to cure it might be any of the thirty-eight. Once again, there is no real alternative to a full understanding of the individual being treated and the particular emotional states that he or she is experiencing.

WORRY

Those people who hide their anxiety behind a facade of cheerfulness can benefit from agrimony. This is the remedy for those who prefer not to face up to the unpleasant things in life and do all they can to avoid thinking about them. But although they can do this when they are surrounded by a crowd of friends and acquaintances they find that at quiet moments their worries return, leading to sleepless nights full of tormenting thoughts. Agrimony helps these people to take account of and deal with their problems instead of trying to drown them out, and so helps their natural good humour shine forth in a more genuine way.

The white chestnut state also often leads to insomnia. It is characterized by continual mental arguments and unwanted thoughts. Unlike agrimony types, people in this state find no respite in company or indeed in anything else: instead, they are preyed on by worries about things that have happened or might happen, so much so that it is impossible for them to concentrate properly on the things that actually are happening. The remedy is given in this case to help restore mental calm so that, once again, constructive action can be taken to remove the cause of any worries.

Red chestnut is the remedy for a rather different type of worrier. Red chestnut people tend to be overprotective of their loved ones and worry to an unreasonable degree about their safety, imagining all kinds of disasters and accidents on the slimmest of pretexts. Their worries not only disrupt their own lives but actually harm the people they love, especially when the latter are by nature in the power of the red chestnut person: children especially can be overprotected so that they are denied the chance to grow up into responsible adults. The remedy works to ease unreasonable fears so that the sufferer can inspire courage and confidence in others, instead of undermining these qualities with exaggerated concern.

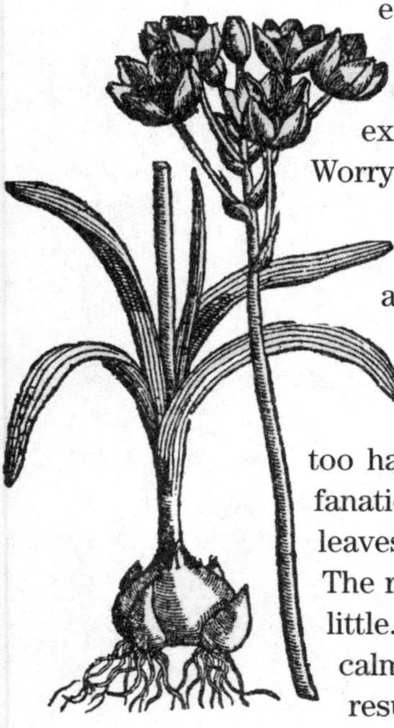

Worry over the welfare of others takes a different form in vervain people. Here it is not the safety of loved ones that is of concern so much as an anxious desire to see social justice and fairness to all. There is nothing wrong with this, of course, but vervain people in their negative state tend to drive themselves far too hard, and their adherence to causes can end in fanaticism. They don't know when to stop, and this leaves them unable to relax and under great stress. The remedy helps teach the sufferer how to let go a little. The same causes may still be pursued, but in a calmer frame of mind that is more likely to achieve results and less likely to lead to illness.

CHAPTER 9

Flower Remedies for Women

There is nothing especially masculine or feminine about fear, uncertainty or impatience, just as there is no age barrier to feeling nostalgic or angry. This means that the remedies for these emotions can be given to all sorts of men, women and children. Indeed, as you will see in chapter 12, even animals and plants can benefit from the remedies, since they too suffer their traumas and sometimes need help to regain their normal healthy balance.

Nevertheless, there are some problems that apply particularly to specific groups of people, and it is to these that we now turn. Chapter 10 looks at problems especially associated with men, such as hair loss and the transition from work to retirement, and suggests the remedies that different types of people can most benefit from when faced with these challenges. Chapter 11 examines the milestones in a child's life, from sleeping problems, to starting school, to dealing with exams – and again details the help that the flower remedies can give.

This chapter deals with women. Because flower remedies are not aimed at physical problems but at the mental and emotional conditions that cause them, they are uniquely placed to help at times when conventional medicine can do little but, in that revealing phrase, let nature take its course. Menstruation, childbirth, the menopause and bereavement: all are normal occurrences in a normal woman's life and as such are not usually thought of as candidates for medical intervention. But the flower remedies are different. They do not seek to get in the way of the processes for which they are prescribed. Rather they act on the state of mind of the person undergoing the process so that, however hard or unpleasant the journey may be, a positive result can be achieved and the individual left stronger and better. For this reason, they are ideally suited to help people cope with the pain and suffering so often associated with the normal cycles of life.

PREMENSTRUAL TENSION

Premenstrual tension (PMT) is the term used to cover any of a number of different symptoms experienced in the days before a period starts. These might include tiredness, irritability, headaches, depression, poor self-image and nervous tension; all of which can occur because of the rapid hormonal changes taking place in the body.

The trouble is that knowing why you feel so out of control does not in itself help to stop the feelings. Some women suffer so badly from premenstrual tension that their intolerance of even the simplest question from a friend or partner can lead to anger and at times to violence. For such cases cherry plum is indicated, as this is the remedy for those who have lost control of their emotions and are afraid they might do *violence to themselves or to others. Fortunately most women do not suffer to this extent from PMT, but the flower remedies are not just for extreme cases, and wherever there is any problem associated with the coming on of a period they are there to help. The key as always is to prescribe for the whole person and the emotional state rather than for the apparent problem.

Anyone who is talking about suicide or any other violent act should be taken seriously. Such people should seek the advice of a doctor, psychiatrist or other counsellor at the earliest opportunity.

For those women who tend to suffer most from depression at these times, mustard can be given. This may generally be preferred to gorse or gentian, because the depression in the case of PMT has no basis in the person's life – nothing has happened to leave her depressed – but rather it is a descending gloom that comes from nowhere and leaves, when it leaves, in the same way.

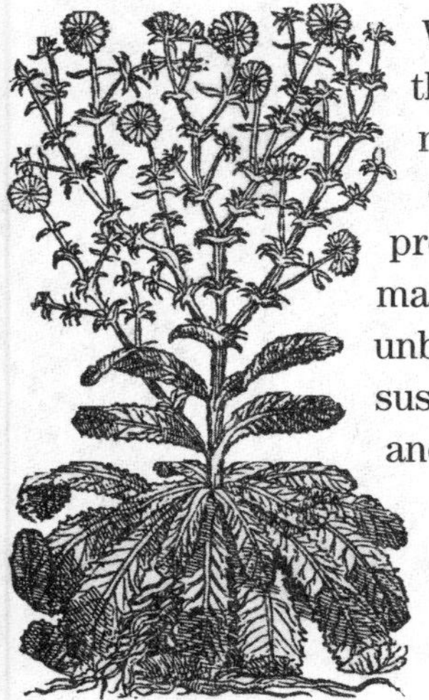

Where impatience and irritability at every delay are the problem, impatiens is the remedy to soothe nerves and do away with those short-tempered outbursts that go as quickly as they come. Where the problem is more one of intolerance, so that the little mannerisms and gestures of other people become unbearable, then beech may be given instead. The more sustained enmity that causes spiteful feelings of hate and anger indicates the need for holly; but if the anger is slow-burning, resentful and full of self-pity, then willow should be preferred.

Where PMT leads to lethargy and tiredness hornbeam is the likeliest remedy to consider, since it is for those weary feelings that do not have a basis in any physical effort but rather come at the mere thought of taking some action. This remedy helps to provide the impetus needed to continue with one's everyday life – and as soon as this initial effort has been made the tiredness itself more often than not fades away.

Finally, crab apple is the remedy to counteract any feelings of self-disgust that might arise, whether psychological or simply due to the fact that you are not feeling at your best. This remedy can also be applied externally in cases where spots or greasy skin are part of the PMT syndrome: simply add two drops of the remedy to fresh water and apply to the affected areas with a clean cloth.

DIETING

Dieting is not in itself a problem, and may even be the answer to a problem where someone is excessively obese and so runs a greater risk of ill health. Neither is it an exclusively female concern, since men too diet, and for as many different reasons as women. Nevertheless, the fact is that most dieting is done by women, for all kinds of social and psychological reasons, and as such the subject belongs in this chapter.

The remedies do not, of course, have any direct physical effect and as such cannot help people to lose weight. What they can do is treat the emotional problems that may be stopping someone from pursuing a diet successfully. And in those cases where the dieting is itself a symptom of some underlying conflict the correct remedies can be selected to address that conflict, and so indirectly treat the obsession with self-image that is usually at the heart of excessive dieting.

The specific remedies to select depend entirely on the personality and emotional state of the person being treated. For example, there is the woman who is forever starting the latest fashionable diet, but each time gives up and reverts to her former eating habits and so never makes any real progress. She might well be a chestnut bud type who will find that this remedy helps her to profit from her previous experiences and avoid making the same mistakes again. Then there is the procrastinator – the woman who is always on the point of starting a diet but never seems actually to get round to doing so. For her hornbeam is indicated, since this is the remedy for people who are always putting things off till tomorrow.

Where someone has managed to start a diet but is not making the progress she had hoped, gentian can be given to counteract any discouragement and so help the person to go on in an optimistic frame of mind. Where the lack of progress is met with impatience rather than discouragement, so that the dieter is inclined to give the whole thing up in a fit of irritability, then impatiens is the remedy to select. And where a failure has left someone short of confidence, so that she feels she will never succeed and does not want to try again, larch is the remedy to give her the courage to make another attempt.

In all the examples looked at so far it has been assumed that the dieting is a reasonable response to a genuine weight problem. Where this is not the case, for instance in cases of anorexia nervosa or bulimia, or simply where a person's concentration on dieting seems out of proportion to her actual body weight, then the dieting itself is probably a symptom of another underlying problem, and it is this that the remedies can be used to treat.

In many such cases crab apple can help. This is the remedy for those who dislike themselves and feel disgust at their appearance. Crab apple people share a trait that is common in those suffering from anorexia nervosa, in that what they see in the mirror is not a true reflection of what they are: because they feel fat and unattractive, they will continue to see themselves as fat long after the rest of the world considers them walking skeletons. Crab apple helps to cleanse feelings of this type so that sufferers can see themselves and their problems in their true light, and so begin to like themselves again.

Sometimes excessive dieting can be an indirect plea for attention by women who do not feel that they are loved enough. Chicory might be indicated in this case, especially where there is an element of cunning and calculation in the actions of the person. Other remedies that might be considered include larch, where a total absence of self-confidence leads the person to believe she is not worthy of attention in her own right; and cerato, which can be given where attention is sought as a way of reassuring the sufferer of her worth.

A third type of person who might get into trouble with dieting is the one who hurts herself in order to find an outlet for her anger at others. People like this feel that their family or their partners have harmed or mistreated them; they want to use their self-

inflicted suffering as a means of making them guilty. It's as if they are saying: 'Wait until you see how sick I'm making myself – then you'll be sorry!' More or less open hatred indicates the need for holly, which would be replaced by willow if there is smouldering spite and resentment.

INFERTILITY

Most women spend a fair proportion of their adult lives trying not to get pregnant. Given this, it is a cruel irony that so many couples will experience some difficulty when they do decide to start a family. Typically, about 10 per cent of women of childbearing age are infertile – or, to be more exact, subfertile, since most are in fact able to have children even though it might take them longer than they expect to get pregnant. And of course infertility is by definition a problem experienced by couples rather than by individuals, so even if the woman's ability to conceive is perfectly normal there might be a problem on the man's side, such as a low sperm count, which can leave a perfectly fertile woman feeling the same emotions of longing and frustration.

In any case, the realization that there might be a problem generally comes slowly, and it may take a year or more of fruitless trying before the nagging doubts start to grow into real concern and lead to a visit to the doctor's surgery.

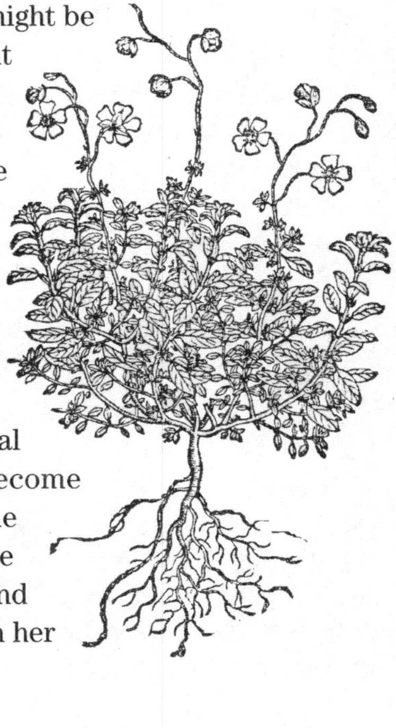

The remedies can help at all stages of this distressing time. Gentian can be given, for example, to counteract any discouragement felt after repeated failures to conceive; or gorse where these feelings are shading towards real hopelessness. Where the desire to become pregnant leads someone to become obsessed with her treatment, so that she talks and thinks of nothing but herself and her problem, heather is the remedy to turn her thoughts outwards to others.

It is hard to overestimate the depth of emotion aroused in a woman when she is denied the chance to bear a child. It is understandable, then, that such strong feelings can take a negative form, leaving her resentful and full of bitterness, especially when friends all seem to have had their babies and she feels she is the only one in her group who has 'failed'. Willow is indicated for this state, and for any tendency to withdraw into self-pity. Where the negative emotions turn into outbursts of temper or violence, holly should be substituted for willow, as this is the remedy for feelings of this sort.

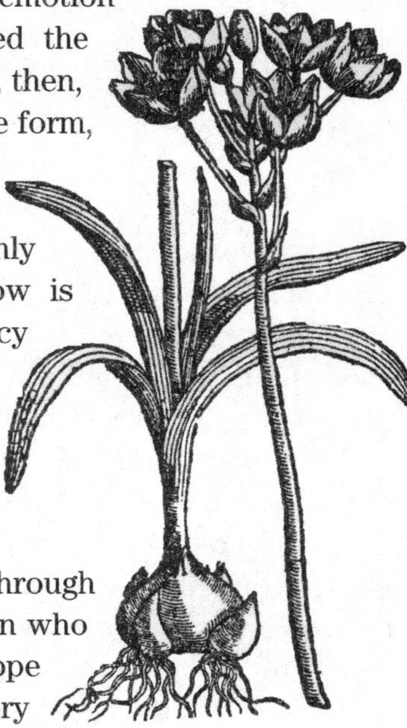

There are many techniques available through conventional medicine that can help women who not so long ago would have had to give up hope of ever having a child. Thus there is every reason to hope and to go on trying. What is more, all shades of medical opinion agree that the worst thing a woman faced with this problem can do is become too obsessive or downhearted about things. There are many cases on record of couples who conceived precisely at the moment when they had resigned themselves to remaining childless, and so ceased trying. The lesson seems clear: the best frame of mind in which to conceive is your normal frame of mind. As this is exactly the condition the remedies work to create, they are ideal helpers in the search for a child of your own.

PREGNANCY

Most women would probably rate the time they first knew they were pregnant as a pivotal moment in their lives. But reactions to the news can vary wildly. For some it is a much desired and well prepared for event. It may even be a huge relief where there have been problems conceiving. But for others the news can be extremely unwelcome, and the baby growing inside can seem to be nothing but an unwelcome intrusion into an already busy and fulfilling life. Whatever the reaction of the individual woman, the flower remedies are ideal helpers, for use throughout pregnancy and beyond, because they are completely safe, natural and non-toxic and will do no harm to either mother or baby.

Any pregnant woman is advised to discuss any intended treatment, including flower remedy treatment, with a qualified medical adviser.

The moment when the pregnancy is first confirmed can be something of a shock. Star of Bethlehem is the remedy for this, but often Rescue Remedy (see chapter 5) might be used as well, and this of course contains star of Bethlehem. The aim of this treatment is to put the person back on an even keel so that rational and sensible thought can prevail.

Another emotion commonly felt at the news is that the mother-to-be wonders about how prepared she is for a new arrival. If she is normally a capable person who momentarily doubts her ability to cope with her everyday responsibilities, elm may be prescribed. But a rather different type of doubt arises in the case of a woman who is not sure whether or not to go through with the pregnancy. In this situation all kinds of contrary emotions can come to the fore, such as guilt (pine), constant worrying thoughts (white chestnut) and shame at one's physical condition (crab apple). For the woman who feels driven to seek the advice and opinions of others, even after she has made up her own mind what to do in these circumstances, cerato can provide the strength of mind to stick firmly to the correct decision once it has been arrived at. Where the consequences of an unwanted pregnancy give rise to fears for the future, mimulus is indicated, or rock rose when the fear is so great it paralyses all possibility of rational thought; and where despondency and gloom take over gentian is needed, or gorse when the state tips over into genuine hopelessness.

Much of the above might seem to suggest that pregnancies are always unwanted, but of course the vast majority are the cause of great celebration. Still, mimulus might again be indicated for many types of fears, from financial concerns caused by the imminent arrival of a new mouth to feed, to the thought that the baby might not be born healthy. In the latter case, red chestnut might be more appropriate, as this is the remedy for those whose anxiety for the welfare of others is exaggerated to the point where it does nothing but harm both the person worried about and the person doing the worrying. And where such unwanted thoughts revolve continually in the mind, effectively spoiling the mother-to-be's enjoyment of her condition, then white chestnut is there to help restore calm.

As the pregnancy nears its end, it is normal to feel extremely tired because of the added weight that must be carried around everywhere. Obviously the only sensible cure for this is to have plenty of rest – but olive can help add extra strength too. For those women who plod on and on, refusing to rest or to hand over any responsibilities to others, so that they overworked themselves, oak is the best remedy. Vervain might be suggested instead for those women who are so full of energy and enthusiasm for their tasks that they refuse or are unable to relax and to pass the reins to others. And for those cases where the mother begins to blame her unborn child for her lack of energy, so breeding resentment, willow is indicated. There is a remedy too for the loss of emotional self-control that can come when all the physical and emotional changes of pregnancy become too much to bear. Cherry plum will help to ease tension and remove the fear of irrationality leading to violence.

Lastly, walnut can be a help for those women who find it hard to adjust to their new status. This is more likely to be the case for those about to have their first babies – but even if there are already children in the family, a new arrival always means an irreversible change in life and the need to break with old habits and find new ways of doing things. As the link-breaking remedy, walnut is the obvious helper for those times when change seems difficult or simply unwelcome.

CHILDBIRTH

Even if the pregnancy has been completely trouble-free and everything has gone smoothly, the birth can still be a fairly traumatic experience. The very surroundings where you give birth can contribute to this, since most people do not feel entirely comfortable in places they do not know well, and hospitals with their monitors and institutional air are often especially disliked. Mimulus can be usefully given to those women who fear hospitals or any of the things that go with them, such as needles, the delivery room or drugs generally.

But the real struggle comes once labour has started. At this time Rescue Remedy (see chapter 5) is the automatic first choice for most women, and it is no exaggeration to say that it is widely used in delivery rooms around the world to help women cope with the pain and shock that can be felt at this time. Four drops put into a glass of cold water and sipped as needed can be wonderfully refreshing as well as helping to deal with the pain. There is no reason why this cannot be combined with the usual pain relief methods such as gas and air or epidural anaesthesia (an injection of painkiller into the area around the spinal cord). It can also be combined with other complementary therapies: some hospitals now regularly offer aromatherapy to women in labour, while massage and the healing benefits of music are if anything even more established.

Immediately after the birth Rescue Remedy can be taken again to speed recovery; and now, just as before birth, the new baby can benefit from the composite as well, for if she is breast-feeding the mother will pass on its healing properties along with her milk. The Rescue Remedy can also be applied to the nipples, where it will not only transfer its benefits to the infant child but will also help to protect against any soreness felt in the early days of breast-feeding – Rescue Remedy cream would of course be particularly useful for this as it is so much easier to apply, and is soothing in its own right. For those mothers who are bottle-feeding their babies, one or two drops of the Rescue Remedy can be added to the first feed, and to subsequent feeds as and when needed.

RETURNING TO WORK

Many women choose to interrupt their careers at some stage in order to raise a family. Once their children have reached a certain age, they are faced with the problem of reintegrating themselves into the world of work. This is perhaps harder to do today than at any time in the past, since the impact of computers and other new technology has changed most offices and factories to such a degree that they are unrecognizable to people who left work a decade or more ago. It can take a great deal of courage and perseverance to catch up with the way things are done now, and this is where the remedies can help.

Different women will react differently to the challenges posed by job-hunting. Some may feel timid and unsure of themselves after a long time away from work. Will they be able to fit in? Will they be able to catch up with the younger generation? For such a lack of confidence, larch is indicated.

Where the person does not doubt her ability to learn new skills and do a job, but rather doubts her ability to decide on the right job in the first place, then cerato is more appropriate, since this is the remedy for those who lack confidence in their judgement. On the other hand, where the process of making a decision between possible alternatives is the main problem, scleranthus is the obvious first choice; but where the alternatives are not clear, so that the person is unable to make any decision as to which career path to follow, then wild oat might be given. This is the remedy for those people who want to do something worthwhile in their lives but, not knowing what that something should be, have a tendency to drift from job to job, so becoming frustrated and bored.

Finally, and just as it may have helped someone to make the transition from career woman to full-time mother, so walnut can now help to ease her move back again.

So far we have assumed that every woman returning to work will have spent a long time away from it – but of course many women return to work a few months or weeks after giving birth, and the situation they face is rather different. The most obvious problem is tiredness. Unless she is very lucky the baby will almost certainly be waking two, three or more times in the night, and even with a partner who does his fair share of the changing and feeding this means a good deal of sleep is lost. Olive is the remedy to help restore lost strength and vitality. Where it is felt that a tendency to take on too many commitments is a contributory factor, this might be supplemented or replaced by vervain if the woman is a hyperactive, zealous type full of nervous energy; or by oak if she is more of a dogged and courageous plodder, who tries to keep going at the same rate long after exhaustion should have persuaded her to rest.

Apart from the physical tiredness, mothers returning to work while their children are still young may do so with very mixed emotions, and it is quite common to feel a measure of guilt about leaving children in the care of others. Pine is the remedy to deal with this negative emotion, so that a woman in this position can decide what is best for her and her children without needless self-blame. Where guilty feelings follow the criticisms of other people, for example those of relatives or friends who either do not need or do not want to go back to work themselves, walnut can be used in its capacity as a guard against adverse outside influences. And for those who have a particular tendency to allow their thoughts and emotions to be coloured by the ideas of others, centaury can be given to encourage and foster an independent view of the world.

MENOPAUSE

Once a woman reaches her late forties or early fifties, the menopause is the next milestone in her life. The 'change' can be very mild and barely noticed beyond a little moodiness and, self-evidently, the end of menstruation. But for some women it can be very uncomfortable, with embarrassing hot flushes, depression and violent mood swings that see the sufferer laughing one moment and crying the next.

The remedies cannot do anything to arrest or turn back the menopause. But what they can do is help women both to cope with the changes they are going through and to approach them in a positive frame of mind. Once this is achieved, any unpleasant symptoms often fade away as the mind and emotions stop trying to fight the change and accept it as a normal and healthy part of living. The symptoms may even disappear altogether, turning a difficult, unpleasant experience into a barely noticed evolution.

The remedy for all changes in life, including this one, is walnut. This helps to break any links with the past that may be getting in the way of a successful step forward. Other remedies are chosen based on the person's personality type and any attendant feelings about the whole process. If the fear of getting old and of the sicknesses associated with old age is troubling her, then mimulus is indicated. A woman whose reaction is one of impatience, as if the menopause is simply an unwanted hindrance to a busy life, could be given impatiens, or vervain if her extreme mental energy drives her to overcommit herself, denying her any rest. If she has a tendency to hide her symptoms from others by putting a brave face on things and continuing to smile and act as if nothing is wrong, then agrimony is indicated. The opposite reaction, that of telling all and sundry about every minor detail of every symptom, and generally of being obsessed with the change to the exclusion of all else, indicates the need for heather.

A fairly common reaction to the onset of the menopause is a sense of loss and regret for one's youth and for the ability to give birth. Where these regrets cause a woman to live in the past and so neglect the present, honeysuckle can help her to let go and move on. If the menopause has arrived early for some reason, there may be resentment as well, coupled perhaps with bitterness towards other women of the same age who may still be planning families. Willow is the remedy for such negative emotions.

Finally, there is a remedy for the mood swings that can happen at this time in a woman's life. This is scleranthus, which can help to give the menopausal woman a better sense of proportion so that she can move forward without hesitation into the next stage of her life.

BEREAVEMENT

Bereavement is not of course a state peculiar to women, but as women tend on the whole to live longer than their husbands it is included here. All that follows is, however, just as applicable to men who have lost their partners.

Perhaps the remedies most often used in cases of bereavement are sweet chestnut and star of Bethlehem. The former is for the extreme anguish that the event so often causes, when the surviving partner feels as if there is no point to going on with a life that is empty and meaningless. Sweet chestnut can help to lift the gloom and let the person go forward again with at least some measure of hope and expectation.

Star of Bethlehem, on the other hand, is for the shock that bereavement always causes, whether the loved one has died suddenly or after a long illness. Because of this it is usually the first remedy given. It helps to overcome the numbness that people commonly feel, so that the grieving process – itself an essential part of healing – can begin sooner. Dr Bach called it 'the comforter of pains and sorrow'.

These are the commonest reactions to the death of a loved one. But both shock and the terrible despair of the sweet chestnut state can be replaced or compounded by all sorts of other emotions. These might include guilt, the tendency to live too much in the past, resentment, or doubts of one's ability to cope with everyday responsibilities.

Guilt is one of the commonest of these reactions. Typically it is felt because of some past action or inaction that might have hurt the dead person. Sometimes the guilt is based on an actual event; at other times the sufferer might be completely blameless; but in any case the emotion often manifests itself at this stage precisely because there is now no easy way to atone for the guilty action. It is as if the person is punishing herself – perhaps because she feels there was something she could and should have done to avoid the loved one's death.

Guilt at this level can very easily strip all joy from life. The flower remedy pine is indicated in such cases to comfort the grieving person, let her forgive herself for her real or imagined misdeeds, and come to terms with herself and her life once more.

The opposite side of the pine state is, in this instance, the willow state. Just like the grieving pine person, the willow person wants to blame someone for what has happened, but instead of taking everything on herself she turns all her resentment and bitterness against other people – or even against the person who has died. Instead of bemoaning the loss of past happiness, she grumbles incessantly about her present condition and about how hard things are for her now that the other person is dead. And instead of wanting to punish herself more than anyone else, she would prefer it if everyone were as miserable as her.

The willow flower remedy is used to resolve the self-pity and frustrated anger that lie behind this state, so that the person can move forward in a clearer frame of mind and slowly begin to rediscover the joy in her own life, as well as rejoicing at the joy in other people's.

As introspective as the willow state is that of the honeysuckle person. This arises where the natural desire to think back to more pleasant times spent in the company of the loved one becomes morbid and excessive, so that the grieving person begins to live in the past and pays no mind to the present or the future. The action of the honeysuckle remedy is to lead the attention back to the present so that the grief can be lived through now, experienced and allowed to fade naturally.

Finally, and for the feelings of helplessness that may come when one is left alone for the first time, elm can be a great comforter. For example, this remedy is indicated for those women – usually older women – who have perhaps never had to deal with financial affairs, or mend a broken fuse or change a wheel on the car. If they are left alone suddenly they may at first doubt their ability to cope, and the elm remedy helps to remove such self-doubt.

These are just a few of the remedies that can help at this sad time. As always, others may be indicated for particular character types and specific states of mind.

There is more information in chapter 4 (the alphabetical guide to the remedies) on how to go about choosing remedies for different types of people and different emotional states.

CHAPTER 10

FLOWER REMEDIES FOR MEN

Most of the problems dealt with in this section may be faced by women too. Nevertheless they are most often associated with men, whether for biological reasons – as with hair loss, for example – or sociological ones. So while women too may find difficulty dealing with their emotions or find the transition from work to retirement a problem, these problems are listed here because the majority of people suffering them will be men. However, in all that follows the indications provided can be applied to both sexes.

Remember that in all cases the suggested remedies are not the only ones that can be used, and that there is no single remedy or combination of remedies that can be used in every instance of a problem. The key to choosing the right remedies is always to get below the surface and look at the whole person and his reactions to the situation. This means that there will undoubtedly be times when a remedy other than those listed will be needed. This is especially true where the apparent problem – fear of retirement, say – is actually the symptom of a deeper underlying cause, for such a cause may be entirely different in character.

DEALING WITH EMOTIONS

When they are growing up, boys are often encouraged not to show their emotions. If they cry or blush too easily they may be labelled 'cissies' and become the target for name-calling and bullying. It is hardly surprising, then, that so many men are unwilling or unable to deal with their feelings successfully, preferring to retreat behind a show of indifference rather than risk being seen as weak.

The situation has perhaps improved a little with the much-heralded advent of the New Man. But ours remains a culture that glorifies male toughness and ruthlessness, as any trip to the cinema will quickly demonstrate. What the films don't so often tell us is that not being able to vent emotions can cause any number of problems, such as stress, loneliness, anxiety and tension. All of these in turn can lead to physical illness – but perhaps the worst result of this kind of repression is that the person concerned cuts himself off from one of the richest and most life-enhancing forms of self-expression. The remedies are there to help free the blockage, so that emotions can be expressed and communicated more successfully, releasing stress and increasing the individual's sense of being part of a community based on mutual care.

It is impossible to generalize in the case of the flower remedies, of course, and the actual remedies to use will always depend on the individual case being treated. But as an aid to selecting remedies, here are some that you might want to give special consideration to.

First of all, agrimony is the remedy for those who try to hide their troublesome emotions behind a smile. It is indicated for those who seem to be the life and soul of the party and are always laughing and joking but who, when they are on their own, find that the feelings they have been trying to drown out return. Since this often happens at night, they may suffer from insomnia. Drink and drug abuse are also relatively common.

For those people who are very strict with themselves, who set themselves high standards of self-control and are hard on themselves if they betray them, rock water might be indicated. Rock water people tend to be wound up tight, and the remedy helps them to relax and be more at ease with the way they are. This allows them to show their emotions more easily, as they no longer feel that they should always be setting an example of self-control to others.

Rock water people do not as a rule interfere with others, since they are too wrapped up in their own search for perfection. Vine types, however, have no hesitation in riding roughshod over other people in order to get their own way. Their desire is for authority and power, and as such they tend to show a hard face to the world. Their inability to look with compassion on other people's needs is linked to their ruthless suppression of natural emotion in themselves, so curing the first problem inevitably involves treating the second. This the remedy achieves by adding insight and understanding to the person's natural gifts for leadership and decisiveness.

Other remedies that you might consider to help men with their emotions include cherry plum, where the fear of losing self-control is the cause of their clamping down on their feelings; beech, where a love of order and control is coupled with intolerance of those who do not share these traits; and centaury, for people who are so put-upon and influenced by stronger characters that the emotions they do show are often pulled out of shape by convention or by the opinions of other people. Finally, for those people who are simply afraid of the strength or the flavour of their emotions and so try to repress them, mimulus can be given.

HAIR LOSS

Hair loss – or, more correctly, ways of reversing hair loss – has probably given rise to more quackery and misleading claims than any other problem mentioned in this book. So it might be as well to stress again that the flower remedies do not treat physical conditions and that there is no question of the remedies somehow stopping hair loss, still less of their reversing the process once it has begun. What the remedies can do is help people going through this change to come to terms with things. In this way the process can be lived through in a positive way. By removing the stress and worry associated with the problem, the psychological causes that can speed up the loss are themselves reduced or eliminated. This can help to slow down the physical change.

Men differ widely in their reactions to losing their hair, but perhaps worry is the commonest state of mind that the news provokes. The remedy to choose where this is the case depends on the type of worry involved. If it is non-stop, so that the problem gets in the way of thinking about anything else and prevents the person concentrating on other matters, then white chestnut could be the remedy to select. Where someone hides his worries behind a mask of cheerfulness, even laughing and joking about going bald, but in private agonizing over the prospect, then agrimony can be chosen. But for those people who become self-obsessed to the point where they begin to discuss the problem with all and sundry, so that others might actually start to avoid them, heather is indicated.

Part of the problem with losing hair is of course that it represents a sign of ageing and the loss of youth. People for whom hair loss triggers a general sense of nostalgia and regret for lost youth – and lost opportunities – can benefit from the action of the honeysuckle remedy. Where it is the loss of a youthful appearance that is the heart of the problem, gentian can be given to overcome the feelings of despondency and discouragement that arise, or larch where the person feels that he is no longer able to do things: hair loss is often associated with a (usually temporary) loss of confidence.

To counteract any tendency to feel resentful about others who are not going through this change, willow can be a help. And where the person feels he can no longer stand to look at himself in the mirror, then crab apple is the remedy to help deal with this tendency to self-disgust. In all cases walnut can be usefully given to anyone who is having trouble adapting to any change, including this one. Its action is to break the links with the past that prevent the person from seeing this change – like any other – as a chance for new growth and maturity.

So far we have looked at people who suffer hair loss in their later years. However, some people undergo this change when they are much younger, in their early twenties or even on occasion in childhood. If it is hard for a mature man to accept the loss of his hair, it is naturally much worse for someone whose age has in no way prepared him for the event. For the shock involved in this case, star of Bethlehem would be the first remedy to turn to. Again, walnut could be added to help the person cope with the inevitable changes. Other remedies can be added as necessary, and many of them have already been mentioned: larch to restore confidence; willow for lingering resentment, or holly for the anger and hatred that can be the explosive development of the willow state; wild rose where the unexpected event leaves the person apathetic and feeling there is no point even trying any more; and gorse for the despair the young man may feel on being told that there is no final cure for the condition.

COPING WITH PRESSURE

This is another of those problems that can be felt by women as much as by men. Nevertheless, most of the victims of heart disease, strokes, high blood pressure and other disorders associated with the inability to cope successfully with pressure are men. Issues such as whether women simply deal better with pressure, or whether continuing social inequality means that women do not as often have to deal with work-related stress, are not questions for this book. What concerns us here are the emotional states and characteristics that stop people from dealing with stressful situations, and this is where the flower remedies can have a beneficial effect, by helping the person stay balanced and rational in the face of pressure so that sensible decisions can be taken without too much panic or stress.

For those who try to conceal the effects of pressure behind a facade of laughter, agrimony is the indicated remedy. It helps such people to overcome and cope with the effects of pressure without them having to resort to drugs or drink in order to quieten their tormenting thoughts.

Elm and oak people can find that their very ability to cope with responsibility leads to them being put under pressure, since others assume that they will always be able to deal with just one more task. Then, when things become too much for an elm person, they can feel suddenly overwhelmed by all the things they have agreed to do and so come to doubt their ability to do them at all. Oak people, on the other hand, plod on and try harder, with the result that when the breakdown does come it is all the worse. Their respective remedies help these different types to get on with their lives with renewed confidence and strength.

Vervain people also tend to overwork, because they are enthusiasts whose commitment knows no limits. They can become so worked up about things that they are unable to relax. It is at this stage that the remedy can be called on to release the continual, largely self-imposed pressure. The impatiens remedy has a similar effect on impatiens people, who are also forever on the move because of their impatient desire to get things done. Like vervain types, they are themselves largely responsible for the pressure they live under, since they hurry everything and become immensely frustrated with any delay. The remedy helps them to slow down a little and develop patience.

Many other remedies may be used in particular cases to help men who are suffering from pressure, whether at work or at home. In all cases the key is to select them on the basis of the individual's needs and to take into account the person's basic character type and his emotional state. Bear in mind too that someone who says he is suffering by being under too much pressure may in fact have some deeper underlying problem that is not immediately apparent. If this is the case, it is the underlying problem that you need to treat. The effects of pressure in such instances are merely symptoms and can effectively be disregarded.

THE MID-LIFE CRISIS

As the term suggests, the mid-life crisis tends to come during a man's middle years; and is often particularly associated with his fortieth birthday. Its other name – the male menopause – neatly captures the fact that many of the psychological symptoms are much the same as those a woman suffers at the same stage in life: lethargy, tiredness, irritability and nervous tension. As far as we can tell, however, the male menopause is not a physical problem so much as a mental one. A man going through a mid-life crisis is someone who is questioning who he is, what he has become and where he is going. More particularly, he is someone who is finding that the answers are not exactly what he would have wished. Knowing that his youth has finally ended, for the first time his thoughts turn towards his own mortality, and time, which hitherto has seemed endless, suddenly seems all too short. Coupled with this, he will also be noticing the changes in his own body: he might no longer be able to run for a bus without suffering for it; he may notice his muscle tone becoming worse; and he may develop the dreaded middle-age spread.

All this sounds very negative, and to the man in this state of mind it is hard to find much of a silver lining in the cloud. Consequently he may try to escape the situation. For some men the escape attempt can be as trivial as buying a new suit; others may suddenly change career or abandon lifetime partners almost on a whim.

These are the problems, then, and as with the true (female) menopause the remedies are very well placed to help, since they deal directly with the emotional state.

Where the main cause of discontent is felt to be the person's lack of direction in life, wild oat might be given. This is the remedy to help people find their true vocation, and is indicated in those cases where the person has tried various different careers but has never found one he could follow wholeheartedly. Chestnut bud might also be useful where obviously inappropriate choices have been made repeatedly in the past, since this is the remedy for those who habitually repeat their mistakes because they are unable to learn from them.

Wild oat could also be given where a relationship is the focus of the menopausal man's discontent, as the remedy helps in finding the path in this as in all life's important questions. Cerato may be given instead where the person in his heart knows whether or not the relationship should continue but simply lacks confidence in his own judgement. Where the problems are caused by his intolerance of his partner's way of life or behaviour, beech could be given, with willow or holly substituted for this if intolerance and irritability have given way to stronger, more negative emotions: smouldering resentment in the case of willow, or open anger and hatred in that of holly.

In all these cases the result of the treatment is not completely foreseeable. The man who is considering giving up a well-paid job to go off and be a sculptor may seem foolish, but if this is what he really wants to do then he should go ahead and do it. The flower remedies will not dissuade someone from an action – what they will do is allow the person a more balanced frame of mind in which to see the results of the action and, once a decision has been taken, provide the courage and strength of will needed to carry that decision through.

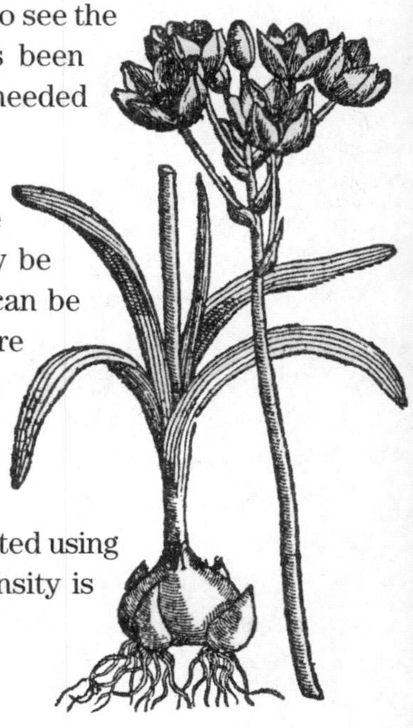

The remedies dealing with fear might be used where this seems appropriate. For example, the fear of getting old and of illness and death may be particularly strong at this time. All these fears can be treated with mimulus, but in some cases – where the fear of death becomes morbid and exaggerated, for example – aspen might be more appropriate. Where the realization that one has already lived through half one's life causes a stronger fear or panic, this might be treated using rock rose – although a fear of the rock rose intensity is not normally associated with the mid-life crisis.

Depression is another problem. Often this seems to come out of the blue, and the man is unable to give any reason for his feelings. In this case mustard is the indicated remedy to restore inner peace and lift the black clouds that have descended. Where the depression is more reasonable – in other words, the man is depressed because he is getting old or for any other reason that he can put a name to – then either gentian or gorse can be given: the former for that somewhat melancholic or downhearted mood when one feels discouraged and inclined to pessimism; the latter for the more dramatic hopelessness when one feels that nothing can be done to solve the problem.

Other flower remedies that could be called on at this stage of a man's life include cherry plum, for those moments when desperation leads him to fear that he might lose control; and crab apple, which can be given for any tendency to self-hatred and for a poor self-image generally. This latter might be especially important where it is the physical changes in the man's body and the loss of strength and looks that are at the heart of his negative reaction to growing older. Finally, for the feelings of guilt that can arise when he looks back and takes stock of his past, pine may be indicated.

RETIREMENT

Some people seem to ease into their retirement years with barely a second thought. Others relish the chance of dedicating their time to some special interest. But there remains a substantial minority for whom retirement is something to be dreaded. For such people the remedies can prove a great help in achieving the necessary adjustment both more quickly and as painlessly as possible.

As might be expected, the first flower remedy that comes to mind in this case is walnut, the link-breaker. This is the remedy for all those situations in which progression is blocked by ties to the past or old ways of life. As well as being used in its own right, it can also be added as a helper remedy with other remedies that might be prescribed according to the individual's character or other elements in his mental state.

For those for whom the thought of retirement brings fear of the future, fear of having nothing to do, or simply the fear of old age, mimulus is indicated. Where the fear seems groundless or irrational, aspen might be given instead. This could be the case, for example, where a person becomes morbid as soon as he retires and starts to feel an exaggerated fear of death and disease, even though he seems perfectly healthy. Where the fear takes the form of an overconcern for the welfare of those around him, such as worrying unduly about whether or not his wife and children will be able to cope without his financial input, then red chestnut is the remedy to choose.

Men who are used to positions of authority and responsibility can be particularly hard hit by retirement. Elm people, for example, may find that the thought of one day laying down their responsibilities leaves them feeling uncharacteristically unsure of themselves and worried that they will not be able to cope with things they would normally take in their stride. Oak types, on the other hand, plod on with their daily toil, putting aside any worries they have about retirement. The result can be that their retirement day creeps up on them, as it were, so that they are not as well prepared as they might be and suffer something of a crash when they can no longer carry on working but have to accept changes. For both these types, the remedies' task is to restore people to themselves so that they can take stock and plan for retirement. In this way, when it comes they will be able to cope with it in their usual solid way.

Vine people too can find retirement hard to take. Used to the role of leader and voice of authority, vine types can find it hard to adapt to a domestic role, and may be inclined to try to usurp power at home now that they can no longer wield it at work. Such people can become petty tyrants, and of course this does not do a great deal for family relationships. The remedy in this case is called on to soften the vine person's tendency to authoritarianism and temper it with understanding and an interest in other people's wants and desires.

Other types of men might find the transition to home life leaves them inclined to sink into triviality. It is all too easy to spend a whole day doing the washing up, or to worry unnecessarily about the cost of a joint of meat or what the neighbours are up to. For such obsessive thoughts and actions, crab apple is the remedy. As the cleansing remedy, it is the ideal choice to wash away the humdrum compulsions that can, if left untreated, see the sufferer wasting the opportunities of retirement.

For those who sink into lethargy once they leave work, wild rose can help. This is the remedy for apathy, and can be given to men who see little point in doing anything at all now that their working days are over. Where the case is not so severe, and the person feels not so much apathetic as weary at the thought of the coming day, so that it becomes a great effort to get out of bed in the morning, hornbeam may be given. Finally, for those people who want to do something worthwhile with their retirement years but are unable to find the right thing to occupy them, wild oat is the remedy to help make things clear so that the right path can be found.

These are just some of the problems that can face men. Many others are treated in the general section in chapter 8, where problems are listed in alphabetical order for ease of reference.

CHAPTER 11

Flower Remedies for Babies and Children

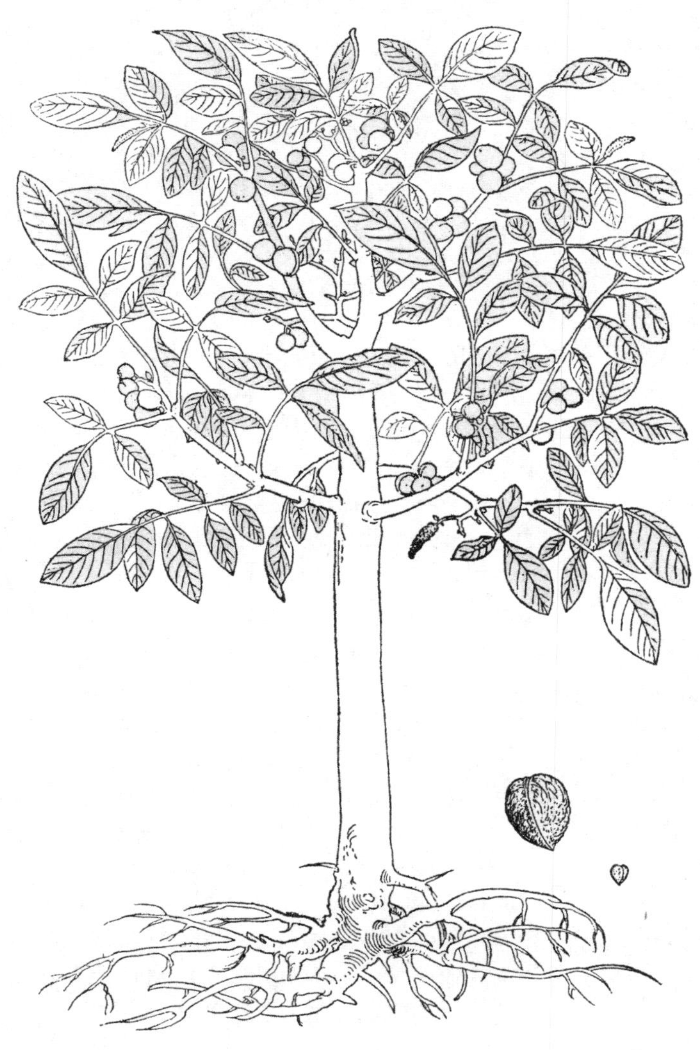

With many kinds of treatment, not least conventional medicine, special care has to be taken when treating babies and children. Simply because of their small size, dosages have to be worked out very carefully to ensure that there are no ill effects and that the cure does not turn into part of the problem.

If you are in any doubt about the physical health of a child in your care, you should get qualified medical advice at once. Remember that the flower remedies are not a substitute for conventional medical care, especially in the case of physical injury. Always follow the treatment instructions in chapter 3, especially when giving the remedies to young children, since the undiluted stock bottles contain almost pure brandy.

With the flower remedies too you should be especially careful when selecting for children. The remedies themselves are of course perfectly harmless and can be given to infants of any age. But the point to bear in mind is that they are preserved in neat brandy, and for this reason you should be very careful always to give the drops diluted in water, as described in chapter 3. Of course, in an emergency you might need to give a few drops direct from a Rescue Remedy stock bottle (see chapter 5), but with children this should be a rare exception to the general rule.

Apart from this one consideration, it is usually easier to help children find the right remedies than it is for adults. This is because children are more open about themselves and how they are feeling, and at the same time they do not have the preconceived notions of what medicine is and what it should do that sometimes interfere with the simple use of the remedies when treating adults.

Having said this, it is obvious that you will have to trust your instincts when prescribing for very young babies, or for any child not yet able to talk. With practice you will soon become adept at second-guessing the reason for any particular emotional state. This seems especially easy to do when the child is your own, as there is usually a definite bond between parent and child that makes it possible for even very young babies to communicate fairly complex emotions without the benefit of words.

Children suffer in the main from the same emotional states as adults. For this reason, and as well as the information in this chapter, you can usefully refer to chapter 8, where there is an alphabetical list of emotional states along with suggestions for treating them. The current chapter looks not so much at the states as at the situations every child is faced with as he or she grows up, and seeks to suggest ways in which the different remedies can help individual children to pass through the various stages as successfully as possible. Before following any of the indications here it is a good idea to refer to the full description of the remedy you are considering, which is given in chapter 4. This will help you decide which of two or more similar remedies are appropriate for the individual for whom you are selecting.

BIRTH

While some births can be relatively quick and easy, there is no doubt that for most new babies (some would say, for all new babies) there is an element of shock and trauma associated with the event – it is after all the equivalent of being forcibly evicted from one world into another that is quite different, full of sound and fury.

Where the mother has been using the flower remedies to help her through childbirth, there is usually no need to prescribe for the baby as well. The beneficial effects of any remedies the mother has taken will be passed on to the baby through the breast-milk. For bottle-fed babies, two drops of Rescue Remedy (see chapter 5) can be added to the first feed, or diluted in a glass of water and used to moisten the baby's lips.

Administered properly, the remedies are completely harmless. Nevertheless, you are advised to consult qualified medical personnel before giving any remedy to a baby.

Instead of the composite Rescue Remedy, the different remedies that go to make it up can be used. Star of Bethlehem is especially appropriate, as it is the remedy for shock, but rock rose for terror, clematis to counteract any tendency to lose consciousness, and impatiens where the baby seems unduly agitated can all be helpful.

Walnut is another remedy that can help both mother and baby at this time. It is the link-breaking remedy, and is used in all cases where a necessary change is made unnecessarily difficult by links to the past and former ways of living. While the mother is helped to come to terms with her new role, the baby benefits by being able to come to terms with its changed surroundings more quickly and wholeheartedly.

SLEEPING PROBLEMS

Few babies sleep through the night in the first few months. More often they will wake two, three or more times in a night, and it may take anything from fifteen minutes to a couple of hours to get them changed, fed and back to sleep again. Where the mother is breast-feeding, or only one parent is present, this can be a very trying time indeed – but even if there are two parents able and willing to take it in turns to see to the baby, this is still a time when anything that might help the child to sleep better will be eagerly grasped at by most parents.

There can be problems too with older children. Nightmares, fear of the dark and simple wakefulness all take their toll next day when the child is unable to concentrate properly at school and so does not do as well as she might. Fortunately, the remedies can help all children of whatever age to regain the peace of mind they need in order to sleep more soundly. And as their effect is in all cases gentle and natural, parents can use them without fear.

Many of the remedies can be helpful where there are problems sleeping, and as always the key is to look for the underlying cause of the sleeplessness. For example, where the child seems to be always on the go and unable to relax, vervain might be indicated. This is the remedy for those born enthusiasts who find it impossible to switch off from their interests. The child who stays up reading or working on some much-loved hobby is one such person, as is the baby who finds the world so interesting that he seems to stay awake twenty-four hours a day. On the other hand, those small children who always seem to need help to get to sleep may benefit from other remedies. The baby who demands two hours' rocking and cuddling before she goes back to sleep could benefit from chicory, which is the remedy for those who demand attention and love all the time. But if the problem is that she is scared of being left alone, then mimulus might be more appropriate, or larch if she is lacking in confidence. Each individual case will be different, and with very young babies it might take a little trial and error before the correct remedy is found.

Worry is a common cause of sleeplessness. For those children who lie awake at night while unwanted, repetitive thoughts circle around their minds, the indicated remedy is white chestnut. This can also be used where endless re-runs of the day's events or rehearsals for tomorrow's are the cause of sleepless nights. And for those children who seem never to have a worry in their head, who are always laughing and joking but who find that repressed worries return when they try to go to sleep, agrimony is indicated. This

Whenever you are dealing with children you should be careful to refer any possible physical problem to a doctor or other qualified medical practitioner.

might also be appropriate for those babies who always seem happy but who at bottom have secret cares that stop them sleeping – but of course you will have to use common sense, intuition and your knowledge of the individual child before making this diagnosis, since the child may be genuinely happy and contented.

Closely allied to worries are fears, and chief among the fears of childhood is perhaps the fear of the dark. There are two remedies that might be used to counteract this. Mimulus, the remedy for named fears, is the first choice on most occasions. But where the fear is not so much of the dark as of all the imagined, unnamed horrors that the child's imagination conjures up within the dark, then aspen, the remedy for vague, unknown fears, might be more appropriate.

Fear is also the problem with those dreams and nightmares that can end in sleepless nights. Bad dreams strike at all ages: just because a child is too young to tell you about a dream it does not mean that there hasn't been one. Consequently the remedy for the terror caused by nightmares – rock rose – could be tried when a baby seems very frightened and yet there is no obvious cause for this. If the terror caused by the nightmare lingers on into apprehension and a vague shifting fear, then aspen is indicated to help dispel the clouds and allow the child to go back to sleep again.

An entirely different kind of problem is seen with those children who find it far too easy to fall asleep, even at times when they should be widest awake, such as an hour or so after getting up in the morning or halfway through a class at school. Clematis is the remedy for those who tend to drift off like this. People of this type are great dreamers who are always making plans for the future but tend to lose interest in the present and so can fail to profit from it. The remedy helps to wake them up so that they can take a more active role in life.

Drowsiness, especially in very young children, can be a symptom of a number of physical problems. If in doubt you should seek qualified medical assistance without delay.

However, not everyone who falls asleep during the day is a clematis type. The problem could simply lie in the child not sleeping enough at night, in which case the remedies above should be considered to see if any of them might apply. Or it could be that the child is taking on too much during the day so that even a night's sleep is not enough. Olive is the remedy to help that tiredness caused by overexertion, but it is worth looking to see if other remedies might be more appropriate in individual cases, such as oak or vervain.

WEANING AND FEEDING

From the age of about three months, babies begin to take solid food and slowly start to abandon their milk-only diet. As with the other stages of their lives, some children make the transition so easily that it is barely noticed; but for others things do not always go so well, and the result can be frustration both for the infant and for the parents.

Once again, walnut can be turned to if the child seems to be held back by ties to the past, but this is not the only remedy that might be indicated. For example, some children can see suckling as a sign of special favour and affection. They like to feel that they are the centre of attention and that all the love available is being directed solely at them. For this reason they go on insisting on being breast-fed long after their contemporaries have stopped. To help in these cases, chicory can be given, as this is the remedy for those whose affections have a selfish slant. It helps the child to let go a little and reassures him that he is still loved even though the breast is no longer offered as a matter of course.

Some children may actually dislike the whole business of taking solids. They do not eat because the process itself disgusts them. In such cases crab apple is the remedy of choice, since it is for those people who feel unclean for some reason.

Persistent problems with eating should be referred to a qualified medical practitioner.

Finally, there is one remedy that can be of use to both parents and children at this time, and that is gentian. This can be taken whenever a setback in the process of weaning and feeding generally leaves those involved feeling very discouraged, as if there will never be any progress. It reassures and lends the confidence needed to believe that the problems faced really are only temporary and will be overcome.

BED-WETTING AND POTTY-TRAINING

Gentian reassures both parents and child that any problems with bed-wetting are only temporary. And of course these are problems that all children face, and all (eventually) overcome. Walnut too can be used, to ease the transition from the security of nappies to the rather riskier world of the potty-trained.

Other remedies that might be selected for children having trouble with toilet training include crab apple, for any feelings of shame and uncleanness after having an accident; pine, for the guilt that can be felt after wetting the bed; and star of Bethlehem, for the shock that an older child might feel if he or she has a setback after a long period of staying dry.

Where toilet training becomes a problem and the child is unable to stay dry despite repeated attempts, then chestnut bud might be considered as well. This is the remedy for those who repeat mistakes and seem not to learn from them. This does not imply that any blame is attached to bed-wetting, or to any other problem with toilet training. It just indicates that the child could use a little extra help to move on and leave this stage behind, and it is this help that chestnut bud can provide.

COPING WITH A NEW BABY

The arrival of a new baby can be a shattering event in a child's life, especially if until now she has been the only child and is used to getting all her parents' attention. If there are problems it can be a very trying time for the parents too, since they are torn between reassuring their elder child and caring for the demanding newborn as well. In extreme cases there might even be the fear that a jealous toddler could do some harm to the baby, so that suspicion and fear take hold at a time when everyone is rather more emotional than usual anyway. The result can be a great deal of family tension.

The flower remedies can be used to help the elder child come to terms with the new arrival and accept that the baby is there to stay. Which remedies to give will of course depend on the child's exact reaction and personality.

For those children who insist on being the centre of attention at all times and become angry and upset when they feel they are being cheated of affection, chicory is the remedy to choose. Chicory people in general are known for the way they will resort to emotional blackmail in order to manipulate their loved ones, and a child in the chicory state is no different. The remedy helps to reassure the chicory child that he is loved and that just because he is not being attended to all the time it does not mean that he is loved any the less.

The chicory child is concerned mainly with the relationship between herself and her parents, but other children will focus more on the new arrival. Jealousy of the baby is common, and for this holly can be given. Disappointment is another fairly common reaction, especially where the child has been told that the new baby will be a friend and playfellow. When the helpless infant proves unable to fulfil the role that the elder child has allocated him, there can be resentment or even anger against the baby or the parents for having pulled such a mean trick. For resentment, willow is the indicated remedy to calm the self-pity and bitterness. Holly may be given to reverse any negative emotions of hatred or anger, while if there is intolerance of the baby's weakness and inability to do things, beech can be a help.

Rather than being intolerant, other children tend to be irritated and impatient at the baby's inability to do the simplest things. For this state of mind impatiens is the indicated remedy. Where there is an attempt to bully the newborn so as to establish the pecking order in the family, vine can be given to strengthen the older child's compassion for and understanding of the baby's needs. And, as at so many other times of change, walnut can help the child to adjust to the new circumstances at home.

If all this seems negative, remember that although it is fairly common for older children to react negatively to a new arrival it is by no means the rule. Even when it does happen the negative feelings usually fade fairly quickly, and with the help of the remedies the time the child takes to come to terms with the way things are will be all the shorter.

STARTING SCHOOL

This is another big change in a child's life, and as such walnut can often be a help at this time. For many children the day they start school may be the first day they have ever spent away from their mothers. The emotional trauma of this, coupled with the strange surroundings and new faces, can make the whole experience very unpleasant, so it is fortunate that with a little thought the flower remedies can be used to ease the transition and cope with the different emotional reactions that can arise.

For those children who are worried about starting school, white chestnut or agrimony is indicated. The former is for those repetitive worries that go through the mind at all hours of the day and night; the latter for the worrying thoughts that recur when the apparently happy child is alone and quiet – usually at night. Both may be the cause of sleepless nights, – an undesirable state in itself – and both can make the days or weeks before school starts an extremely trying time for all concerned.

For those children who frankly fear going to school, mimulus is the remedy to choose. It is also the type remedy for those rather timid, nervous children who fear the thought of being called on to speak in class or become anxious simply at the thought of being in a large group of other children. Children of the mimulus type usually blush easily and may stammer or fidget when they feel that they are the centre of attention. Another group of children, who might appear superficially similar, are the centaury types. They may appear less nervous than mimulus children, but they can easily be imposed on by stronger-minded children and, like mimulus children, they are all too often the victims of school bullies. The remedy in this case helps to give them the independence of mind they need in order to make their own way in school without worrying too much about what their classmates are doing or saying. But even normally confident children can find the first days at school daunting, and in this case larch can usefully be given to bolster the child's flagging self-belief and get her over this initial problem.

Finally, for those children who miss being at home and think of their old routines and the places they used to go with too much longing, honeysuckle is the remedy to give. This can pull them gently back to the present so that they can enjoy and benefit from the experiences of today rather than spending too much time thinking back to the past.

COPING WITH EXAMS

Everyone gets exam nerves to some degree. But whereas a few nerves before a test are actually beneficial, in that they help us to concentrate and so do better than we might otherwise have done, too many can leave the victim unable to concentrate properly and liable to do far worse. Some people can get so wound up before exams that they quite literally make themselves ill, which can end in them missing the chance to take the exam at all.

Rescue Remedy (see chapter 5) is widely used in the run-up to and immediately before an exam. It can be sipped whenever preparations are interrupted by a panic attack or a sudden crisis of confidence, and in such cases quickly counteracts any negative thoughts. It can even be taken into the examination hall and sipped during the exam, preferably diluted in a glass of water – although if you intend to do this you should check first with the people setting or invigilating during the exam to make sure they have no objections.

The other remedy most often associated with exams is larch. This is hardly surprising, as it is the remedy that lends self-confidence to those who doubt their ability to succeed. Like Rescue Remedy, this is most helpful in the period leading up to the exam, and again can be taken just before the exam itself starts.

Other remedies that might be needed during the preparation for an exam include olive, for tiredness brought on by excessive study; vervain, for those people whose very enthusiasm for the subject they are revising can lead them to work too hard and forget to rest, so that they are not at their best on the actual day of the exam; and cerato for the person who spends valuable revision time asking all and sundry about how much revision they think he needs to do.

However, this is only half the story. If the exams pass off without any problem and good marks are achieved, there is little for the remedies to do, unless perhaps wild oat is called on to help the successful student decide on the career she wants to follow. But where there has been a failure or setback of some kind all kinds of negative emotions can arise. Once more, the remedies can help.

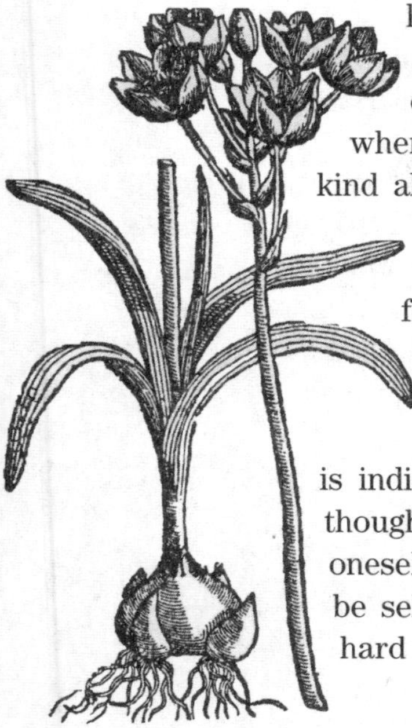

For the discouragement that will inevitably be felt, gentian is the first remedy to turn to. Where things have gone further than this, so that the person feels as if there is no point in trying any more, as it is bound to be hopeless, then gorse is indicated instead. There may be guilt too at the thought of having let down parents or teachers – or oneself – and for this destructive emotion pine should be selected. For those students who are especially hard on themselves because they have set

themselves particularly high standards and feel angry at their failure to meet them, rock water is indicated. And for any tendency to self-pity, bitterness or resentment, whether directed against more successful contemporaries, teachers or the exam system itself, willow can be given.

Very occasionally a true, numbing depression can set in when the person feels as if a failure at an exam has effectively closed the door to the future, leaving everything black and completely hopeless. This is an extreme condition which can lead at times to thoughts of *suicide. In these cases, sweet chestnut for the despair and cherry plum for the violent, suicidal thoughts are the indicated remedies.

P*eople talking of suicide should always be taken seriously, and medical or other qualified assistance sought where necessary.*

In all these cases the treatment goal is to give the student back a clear view of the situation so that he can decide calmly what to do next. The situation is rarely as bad as it appears at first, and there is usually the opportunity to follow some alternative course or even to retake some or all of the failed exams later. To counteract any tendency to fall into apathy, wild rose can be given. Where the student is unable to make up her mind what to do next, scleranthus can also be a help; or wild oat if the options themselves do not seem clear and it is only the desire to do something worthwhile that is apparent.

The transition from childhood to adulthood is a difficult one for both sexes. Children have not had the time to build up great reserves of character and confidence, and so they can sway and bend with every emotional gust. The remedies can be an ever-present help and comfort in these years, not only in the specific situations listed in this chapter, but in all stages from babyhood to adolescence.

CHAPTER 12

Treating Animals and Plants

It can come as a surprise to some that the flower remedies are used to treat animals and plants as well as people. But the principle is the same. In all cases it is the life energy of the remedy plant that is being transmitted, and this can have a beneficial effect on all other forms of life – including animals and other plants.

TREATING ANIMALS

There is obviously one major problem that you will have to overcome if you are going to use the flower remedies to treat animals: the fact that they can't tell you what is wrong. In practice there are two ways round this. The first is to make an educated guess based on your observation of the animal's behaviour and any knowledge you have of its normal behaviour patterns. Imagine, for example, a dog with a bad leg. Is it trying to go on as if nothing is the matter? If so, this might indicate an oak temperament where the continued effort is made in a stout-hearted way, or agrimony where the animal is trying to conceal its discomfort behind lots of tail wagging and play. Another dog might lie in the corner feeling sorry for itself and snapping at anyone who comes too close: this probably indicates the need for the willow remedy. And still another might simply curl up in the corner and take no further interest in anything – a clear case for wild rose.

Obviously this kind of diagnosis is easier to make with a pet, since owners and pets often have a good understanding of each other's moods. One can imagine how much more difficult it would be for most of us to try the same kind of mood analysis with cow number 432 in a field of 500! Not surprisingly, then, many of the case histories to do with the treatment of animals centre on the way remedies have helped pets.

This does not mean that nothing can be done for non-domestic animals. Farm animals have been helped with the remedies too, and there are also many cases of the remedies being used to help wild animals. But in the vast majority of such cases Rescue Remedy (see chapter 5) has been the sole mixture given, and this is the second of the two methods that can be used.

The thinking behind using the Rescue Remedy is that, whatever their individual characteristics, injured or sick animals usually feel some mixture of shock, panic, faintness, agitation and loss of control. As these are precisely the emotions addressed by the different remedies in the Rescue Remedy composite, most if not all cases will be helped to some extent by its application. And this is not really so very different from the way Rescue Remedy is used in a first aid kit to treat people.

Having decided what remedies to give – or having decided on the Rescue Remedy – the next problem is finding a way to administer the remedies to the animal. The simplest way is to mix two drops of each selected remedy – or four drops of the Rescue Remedy – into the animal's water or feed. In the case of larger animals such as horses and cows you should use about five times as much of the stock remedy in a bucket of water – although four drops on a cube of sugar is just as effective, since you can be sure that it will all be taken. The remedy or remedies should be used at regular intervals as long as the animal seems to need it. Just as when giving remedies to people, you may need to review the selection made if there is no improvement, or if the animal's behaviour or mood seems to change.

CASE HISTORY: *You may decide to use the Rescue Remedy first, adding other remedies if this seems necessary. This was done with Cassie, a two-year-old collie bitch who had been mauled by another dog. Within an hour, Rescue Remedy was added to her food. As the wounds were not serious only one dose was given. But when a couple of days later Cassie stopped eating properly and began sleeping during the day, her owner gave her clematis for the drowsiness, and star of Bethlehem for shock. Cassie recovered after a few days.*

TREATING PLANTS

It is of course even more difficult to tell what state a plant is in than it is to analyse an animal. Some hints might be obtained from the plant's condition. For example, a plant that struggles hard to grow back following a savage pruning could be interpreted as needing oak to help it continue to persevere – but one can only go so far with this: how would you begin to tell whether a plant that refused to grow needed mimulus, aspen, gentian, gorse, wild oat, wild rose or any other of the remedies?

Despite these difficulties, there are again numerous instances of the flower remedies being used to help plants recover from all kinds of diseases, parasites and mistreatment. But as you might expect, almost the only remedy used is the Rescue Remedy. Of the ingredients in the composite it is perhaps star of Bethlehem which is most helpful, since it can be assumed that all the problems that occur to a plant produce shock of some kind or another.

Four drops of the Rescue Remedy can be added to water and sprinkled over the plant in the normal way with a watering can. Where there is a localized problem, the mixture can be sprayed directly onto the affected area, or gently wiped on with a clean cloth.

For problems of infestation, such as greenfly, mould, or blackspot, you could try using crab apple. As the cleansing remedy, this can be a good way of clearing away such problems. And where the plant has been repotted or replanted, walnut can help the adjustment to its new surroundings – but here too Rescue Remedy is also an appropriate remedy to give.

CHAPTER 13

Relationships and Sexuality

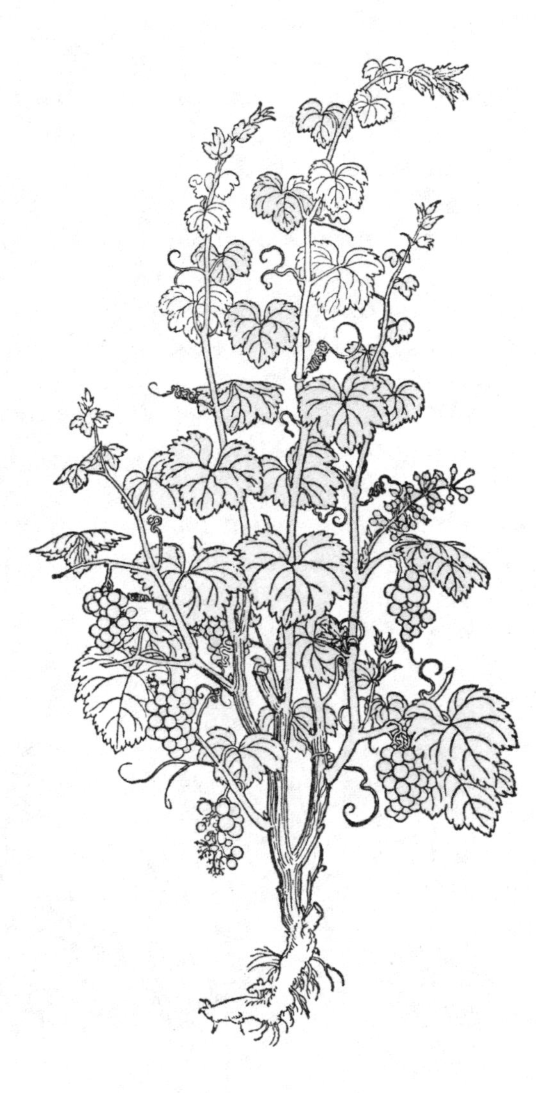

It should come as no surprise that a system of healing that works entirely on the emotional, spiritual and mental level should have much to offer those who are experiencing problems with relationships and with their sexuality. For both men and women, the flower remedies provide a safe and natural way to get feelings under control. With a clearer head, a person is better able to find out what it is that he or she really wants to do, and more able to find the strength and sense of self-worth needed to go ahead and do it.

FALLING IN LOVE

Falling in love is obviously not a problem in itself, and you may wonder why the remedies should have any part to play in the process. If everything runs smoothly they are clearly not usually needed at all, but falling in love can cause all kinds of problems for some people and in some situations, and at these times the remedies can be a real help and comfort.

Perhaps teenagers – or people of any age – who are going through the pangs of first love are the most likely to need help. Larch can help to restore the flagging confidence of those who have yet to declare their passion, while for those who have a poor self-image, perhaps due to a weight problem or some other physical defect which convinces them that they will be rejected, crab apple is the remedy to choose. Once the initial approach has been made, teenagers especially may put their dreams of happiness before other, more mundane matters such as exam results and university places. Clematis is the remedy to keep their feet on the ground so that they do not sacrifice everything for love right away.

There is always the danger that a declaration of interest in someone will be met with rejection. This is never easy to take, but exact reactions to the event vary widely and can include depression (gorse), self-pity (willow), or simply shock (star of Bethlehem). In teenagers a slide into apathy is quite common, where the person rejected stays in his room for days at a time and doesn't want to go anywhere or do anything any more. Wild rose can help at such times. Larch might also be used to rebuild shattered self-confidence. Where the hurt is being concealed behind a devil-may-care facade, agrimony is indicated.

For those who are unsure of their real feelings for someone, scleranthus can help to make things clearer in their minds. Finally, where making a commitment to a relationship involves a choice which could have a profound effect on someone's future, such as abandoning a career or moving abroad, then wild oat can help the person to resolve the dilemma and choose the correct path.

JEALOUSY

For jealousy and suspicion, whether or not there is justification for it, the first remedy to turn to is normally holly. This helps to defuse any anger, so that the situation can be looked at calmly. Chicory may be used instead where the jealousy is unreasonable and based on selfishness – in other words, where the person being treated is trying to control every moment of her lover's life and feels slighted if he gives even a moment's attention to someone or something else. Where the person feels there is good cause to be jealous but is so much under the sway of his partner that he feels powerless to alter the situation, centaury could be given to help him stand up for himself.

In cases where the jealousy is well founded and the offended partner feels there is some real danger of her losing control of herself and committing some violent act against the guilty partner, then cherry plum is indicated.

BREAKING UP

The date that a relationship is actually ended may not be the first day when the remedies can help. Relationships normally take a relatively long time to fail, and along the way there are all kinds of emotions to be dealt with. Jealousy and feelings of rejection have already been looked at in other contexts (see above), but others can be just as difficult to deal with, and as potentially destructive.

Where the end of a relationship involves feelings of guilt on one or both sides, pine is the remedy to select. This remedy helps to remove any unnecessary guilt from the shoulders of those who have a tendency to blame themselves for things that are not really their fault at all – such as the infidelity of a partner, or someone else's decision to end the relationship. And where the person being treated is responsible for the relationship breaking up, the remedy allows him to acknowledge his actions, learn from the experience and then move on. This is essential if his current feelings are not to sour the rest of his emotional life.

Where a person is unable to decide whether or not the relationship should end, scleranthus can help to remove hesitation and make the way ahead seem clearer. Cerato helps those who seek advice from all their friends about what they ought to do when in their hearts they know themselves whether the relationship has any future left.

Where the end of a relationship leaves bitterness and rancour, willow is the remedy to choose. It is also used to counteract any slide into self-pity, or the tendency to contrast one's own woeful condition with the apparently unproblematic happiness of the rest of the world. Holly is given for outright anger – usually forthrightly expressed – at being treated badly. Other feelings allied to rejection might include lack of confidence (larch); concealed hurt (agrimony); despair (gorse); anguished despair as if there is nothing more to live for (sweet chestnut); and apathy (wild rose). However, this list is far from inclusive, for in this as in all other cases the actual remedies to select depend entirely on the character of the individual being treated and on her reactions to the event in question.

DOMESTIC VIOLENCE

Tragically, there are a small proportion of relationships that seem to be based not so much on love as on power and weakness. In cases of domestic violence the remedies have something to offer both sides: the

In most of this book 'he' and 'she' are used indiscriminately. In this section, however, the use of pronouns reflects the reality that most victims of domestic violence are female and most aggressors male. However, the opposite combination can be true, and in these cases the remedies discussed can be used in exactly the same way.

aggressor can be helped to control his anger and end his violence; while the victim can be given the strength to stand up for herself, and if necessary end the cycle of violence by ending the relationship.

There are various organizations set up specifically to help the victims of domestic violence, and anyone in this situation is advised to contact them.

Perhaps the first remedy to consider when treating a victim of domestic violence is centaury. In many ways centaury types are fine people, who want to help others and take little thought for themselves, but unless they have the power to say 'no' they end up no better than slaves. This is particularly likely to happen where they are teamed with more aggressive personalities who have no hesitation in using force to get their own way. The remedy can give them the strength they need to stand up to aggressors and so gain recognition of their own wants and needs.

Some people – usually women – seem to go through a succession of violent relationships, almost as if they are attracted to aggressive partners. For such people chestnut bud might be a help. This is the remedy for those who find it hard to learn from their mistakes, so that they are doomed to repeat them until something breaks the cycle of repetition. For those whose low self-esteem leads them into relationships that they know to be unsuitable, crab apple may be used, as it can help to create a positive self-image and so let the victim know that she can in fact do better.

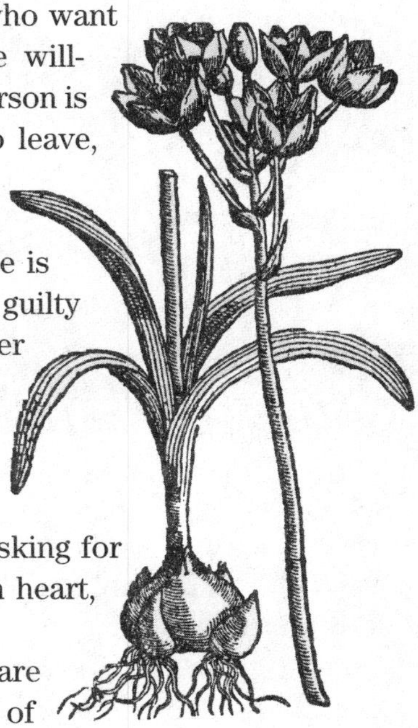

Centaury might also be given to those who want to end a violent relationship but lack the willpower to do so. In other cases, where the person is simply unable to decide whether or not to leave, scleranthus is indicated, as it is for those whose general indecisiveness leaves them unable to choose between alternatives. Pine is the remedy to select where the woman feels guilty about wanting to leave. If she knows in her heart what she wants to do but finds that she is unable to take the step because of some outside influence, walnut is the remedy. And if her lack of faith in her own judgement means that she goes to others asking for their advice instead of listening to her own heart, then cerato may be chosen.

The perpetrators of domestic violence are also a suitable case for treatment. Some of them will turn out to be vine types, who have allowed their natural gift for leadership to become perverted into a drive for domination. Ignoring the wishes of others, they can be cruel and brutal in their methods, so that violence is always an option even when it is not the first one they choose. The vine remedy is given to such people to increase their compassion for others and make them more aware of the effects of their actions.

In other cases resentment and anger lie at the bottom of the violent tendencies, rather than a desire to dominate. Holly is indicated for those whose anger, hatred and envy lead to outbursts of temper. Where the person tends to lose control completely, so that rather than a relatively controlled anger there is uncontrolled violence or the threat of the same, cherry plum is indicated. This is the remedy to help such people master their emotions so that upsets can be dealt with in a rational manner.

Lastly, in the case of both victim and perpetrator there might be some other cause which would explain why each became locked into

the cycle of violence in the first place. This may lie deep in their minds and may be very difficult to bring into the open, but the ultimate success of the remedy course may hinge on your being able to get close to the original problem at least. In some cases it will be found that violence has been part of a person's family life from childhood, and that adult behaviour is just an extension of what was seen and heard in those early years. In a sense these are the simpler cases to select for, since this is the classic pattern of abuse and violence. But in other cases the cause might be wholly different and seemingly unrelated. Here as elsewhere there is no shortcut to successful use of the remedies: you really do have to try to sympathize with and understand the person you are helping.

HOMOSEXUALITY

As homosexuality is not a disease, there is no question of its being 'cured' by any means, let alone by the flower remedies, whose action is to help people live on their own terms and in their own ways. Where the remedies can help homosexual people is in giving them the strength and confidence to come to terms with themselves and their sexuality – and to that extent the following may apply to anyone whose way of life incurs the disapproval or persecution of others.

For those who suspect that they might be homosexual but are unsure and consequently hesitate as to which path to take, there are a couple of remedies that may help. Scleranthus is the remedy for hesitation and doubt in general. Where the hesitation is due to the influence of other people – friends, relations, colleagues and so on – walnut is the remedy to remove any unwanted influences so that such people can tread their new path without being held back. Cerato helps those who find it necessary to seek the approval of others before they can be themselves.

If guilt is a problem, as it might be where the expectations of friends or parents have been upset, then pine is the remedy to choose. This helps to remove the effects of this destructive emotion so that the person concerned does not have his life poisoned by it. Lack of confidence, which leads people to delay telling others the truth or even forces them to live a lie, can be helped with larch, while for those who are actually scared of what other people will think or say, mimulus is indicated. If, having taken the decision to be open about her sexuality, there is a setback that leaves the person feeling downhearted and unsure whether to go on, then gentian is the remedy to help her overcome her temporary discouragement.

Finally, anyone who feels inclined to condemn people for their sexuality (or for their race, their height, or any of the other countless things that people can do nothing about) would be well advised to take a few sips of beech, the remedy for intolerance.

FRIGIDITY, IMPOTENCE AND INHIBITION

Whether problems with sex are mental or physical, the flower remedies can help to clear away the negativity that may lie at the root of the condition. In all cases it is the individual's own character type, coupled with his reactions to the condition, that determine which remedies should be selected.

For those who find the body, sex or sexual relations disgusting, crab apple is the remedy to choose. It works by improving the person's self-image so that she can look beyond any physical problems and see her essential beauty. Crab apple is also indicated where an exaggerated fear of disease leads a person to avoid sex, or where there is an obsessive need for cleanliness and hygiene, with frequent hand-washing and other compulsive behaviour.

For those who are frightened of sex or of allowing themselves to be touched by another human being, mimulus would be the remedy to choose. Cherry plum is given instead when the fear is specifically of the loss of control that sex entails. The action of the remedy in this instance is to reassure the person that his essential being is not harmed but invigorated by the experience, and that there is really nothing to fear in this particular loss of control.

While feelings of fear or disgust at sex can be fairly deep-rooted, others are simpler and usually easier to treat. For example, those who are preoccupied with their performance and so find that they lose confidence in their ability to make love might benefit from larch. Where there is a lack of excitement in the relationship which leaves one or both partners uninterested in sex, wild rose, the remedy for apathy, might help. If the uninterested partner finds that it is the simple thought of making love that leaves her tired, but that she enjoys the experience once it is underway, then hornbeam is the remedy to choose.

Sometimes the problem may be caused by simple tiredness. Elm, oak and vervain people can all find themselves with too much to do, and their respective remedies will help them to regain control at work and so leave more energy for other things. Olive too is a great help where physical tiredness is the problem.

Because our society places such great emphasis on the importance of sex in life, any failure in this area can be emotionally devastating. A vicious circle is quickly set up, when the perceived failure places even more stress on the individual, which in turn makes it more probable that there will be a problem next time. Star of Bethlehem can help deal with the shock caused the first time there is a problem, so that a temporary situation does not have the chance to develop into something more serious. The same remedy can be given for any residual shock left by an unfortunate sexual encounter in the past that might carry echoes into the present. If worries about sex are ever-present, so building up the problem in between attempts at love-making, white chestnut is the remedy to choose; if the worries arise only when the person is alone, agrimony should be selected instead. Rock water helps those who get very uptight about things and so are unable to relax enough to enjoy sex. Finally, for those who find that their natural reserve and love of privacy result in inhibition and make it difficult for them to get close to others, water violet can help.

Where problems with sex are severe or long-lasting, it may help to consult a trained counsellor. You can get advice from your own doctor or, if you prefer, through a family planning clinic, Relate (the former Marriage Guidance Council) or a similar organization. The flower remedies can of course be used in conjunction with whatever other therapy is recommended.

LONELINESS

There are three remedies – impatiens, water violet and heather – that were grouped together and described by Dr Bach as being for loneliness. Of course, this doesn't mean that everyone who feels lonely should take one or even all three of them – you need to look for the cause of the loneliness in order to select the right remedy or combination of remedies – but it does mean that we are perhaps justified in looking at them first.

Water violet people do not mind being alone, as they are self-reliant, self-contained, calm types. They enjoy their own company and many of them choose to avoid relationships and remain single. However, they can find that when they do want other people around there is no one to turn to, since others have seen them happy by themselves and have left them to it. The remedy helps such people to maintain contact with the rest of humanity so that they can mix with others when they choose.

The loneliness of impatiens people is also deliberately sought. These types lack patience with people who are slower than they are and would rather work and live alone than have to put up with being held back and frustrated all the time. As in the case of the water violets, this nature can effectively isolate impatiens people from those around them, so that the freedom to work at one's own pace becomes a trap rather than a release. The remedy helps to reduce the impatiens person's irritability with others so that he can keep the affection of those around him.

The third remedy, heather, is for a very different type of person. Heather people are terrified of being alone, so they seek out company and seem to want to share every last detail of their daily lives with other people. However, their constant talking and tendency to monopolize every conversation is tiring for their listeners, who soon begin to avoid them. The result is that the very thing heather people fear happens to them: they are alone and no one wants to listen any more. The remedy helps the person to offer as well as ask for a shoulder to cry on, and in this way problems are genuinely shared and loneliness vanishes.

Where divorce, the death of a partner or simply the inability to find a partner in the first place leaves someone feeling lonely and unloved, these three remedies can be considered to see if they apply. But, as has been said, other remedies might be indicated instead. For example, where there is despair gorse could be given, or sweet chestnut where the sufferer feels that there is no point in going on alone. Willow is the remedy to give where there is a slide into self-pity or any tendency to resent the happiness of other people. For those who find their confidence has gone, larch can help to restore the sense of self-worth, and crab apple is the remedy to help with any feelings of self-dislike that can arise at times.

For those who simply give up and stop trying to meet other people, wild rose is the remedy to select. Where living alone has left the person with habits that make it hard to meet others, such as staying in all the time watching television instead of going out, walnut can help to break the links that hold her back and give her the freedom to make whatever changes are necessary. For those who shelter from loneliness by living in the past, honeysuckle is the remedy; or, where the sheltering thoughts are dreams of tomorrow instead of flashbacks to the past, clematis may be given instead. Last of all, for those people who have no friends of their own age because they are tied to the possessive demands of an ailing relative or parent, centaury might be indicated to help the person to carve out a life of his own.

FAMILY BREAKDOWN

When a couple divorces, there is almost invariably a great deal of pain and heartache to cope with – and when children are involved the potential for suffering is naturally all the greater. Here again is a situation where careful selection of the flower remedies, according to the personalities and moods of the people involved, can help to minimize the pain and allow everyone to find a new way of life with as little trauma as possible.

Guilt is often a problem when families break up. Where one partner really is to blame, such feelings may be a necessary part of coming to terms with one's actions. But it is also common for the wholly innocent to feel at fault. Children, for example, often blame themselves for their parents' inability to get along together. However much other people may say that there is no reason to feel guilty, it is very hard to get such thoughts out of one's head once they have taken root.

The remedy for guilty feelings is pine. This helps those who genuinely are to blame to come to terms with their responsibilities, while those who have done nothing wrong are freed of an unnecessary burden. Where guilty thoughts prey continually on the mind so that it is difficult to concentrate on the things one is doing now, then white chestnut can be a help as well.

For those who fear the future following a family breakdown, mimulus is the first remedy to consider. Children might benefit more from aspen, the remedy for nameless, vague fears. This is because despite the efforts of parents to shield them from the break-up, children inevitably pick up hints and the general feeling that something is not quite right. The aspen remedy helps them to master the fears that are aroused, so that when they do learn the truth they are at least in a stable frame of mind and so better able to cope.

Often fear might be mixed with feelings of depression or despair. These can range from simple discouragement and melancholy (gentian), through a deeper sense of hopelessness (gorse), to an extremely black mood when life does not seem worth living and the future seems completely empty and bleak (sweet chestnut). Sometimes the person might feel fine most of the time, only to have the depression descend as if from nowhere, as if it has nothing whatsoever to do with the family problems. In this case mustard is the remedy to choose. As in the case of aspen, mustard can also be helpful for those children who have sensed that something is wrong and feel depressed, although they cannot say why this is so.

Obviously family breakdown means that the people involved will have to adjust to a new way of life. At least one of the family members will be moving away – and where the family home is to be sold as part of a divorce settlement, everyone will have to get used to new surroundings. A wife who has been a full-time housewife might find herself having to find paid work again; children might end up switching schools and losing touch with their friends and the area they have grown up in. All of these upheavals can be eased at least in part with walnut, the remedy for times of change. Where the change is blocked by thoughts of the past, walnut can also help, or honeysuckle may be chosen instead, particularly where it becomes difficult to concentrate on today's events because too much thought is given to things that are past.

For those who doubt their ability to cope in the new family structure, larch might be the remedy to choose. Cerato may be given instead where it is one's ability to make sound judgements that is doubted. This could be the case, for example, with the newly divorced wife who finds herself dealing with financial matters that her husband always used to deal with: if she finds herself asking all sorts of ill-qualified people what they think she should do in this or that case, then cerato is the remedy for her. If she feels overwhelmed by all the additional responsibility, elm is the remedy to restore her to her normal self-control so that she can cope as usual.

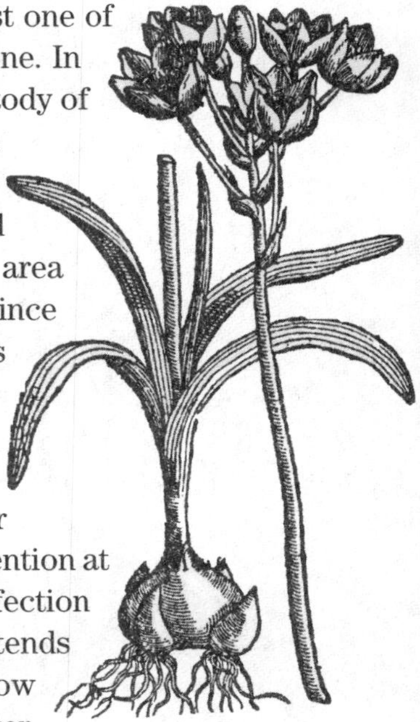

In most cases of family breakdown, at least one of the partners will find him or herself living alone. In practice, because the courts usually grant custody of children to the wife, this tends to be the husband. In this situation loneliness can be a problem, especially if the couple were married for many years or have moved away from the area where they lived when they were single, since there are then less likely to be old friends around who can be relied on to provide companionship. There are several remedies that might help in this case, depending on the type of person and mood involved. For example, those used to being the centre of attention at home who now miss being surrounded by affection might benefit from chicory. Where the person tends to be reserved and private anyway, and now finds it hard to get to know new friends, water violet can help; but for those almost opposite types who talk to anyone – usually at great length – and who fear being alone, heather is the remedy to choose.

Recrimination and ill feeling between family members can be helped by holly or willow. The former is for naked anger, aggression and hatred, while the latter can be used to counteract the more introverted feelings of resentment, bitterness and self-pity.

Any breakdown in family life is bound to be a difficult time for all concerned, but with the help of the remedies it can at least be lived through in the knowledge that there really is light at the end of the tunnel, however black things might seem at the time.

Counselling is available from a number of organizations for both adults and children going through the break-up of a family. Doctors, teachers and clergy will also provide extra support for those who need it. As always, there is no reason why the remedies should not be employed in tandem with any other treatment or therapy that helps.

CHAPTER 14

THE BACH PHILOSOPHY AND THE FUTURE

In many ways Dr Edward Bach was before his time. Believing as he did that it was the whole person rather than specific diseases that should be treated, he was swimming against the tide of 1930s medical orthodoxy. His concept of a natural and gentle approach to medicine was in direct contrast to that of his colleagues who pursued a method based on direct mechanical intervention by way of powerful drugs – many if not all of them actually poisons – and even more invasive surgery. While the scientific method dictated that nothing should be used until it had been dissected, pulled apart and put back together again by artificial means, Bach counselled against the rigorous analysis of method and instead recommended that people accept the flower remedies for what they were – a gift from nature – and take without questioning the benefits they offered.

There have been many people since his day who have tried to make the flower remedy system more complicated and pseudo-scientific. But the greatest success has always attended those who use the remedies as Dr Bach intended, following his recommendation to make things as simple and natural as possible. These are the tried and tested methods that you have read about in this book.

At the end of the twentieth century this formula for health and well-being is at last coming into its own. The more we learn about the way our world works, the more we realize that the holistic approach is everywhere the only path to a more complete solution. Whether treating a cold or safeguarding the planet's environment, the piecemeal approach by itself will never be able to grasp the essential simplicity-in-complexity of life, or of all our lives.

Instead of asking what role there might be for the remedies in conventional medicine, then, we are entitled to turn the question round and ask what

Western conventional medicine can contribute to this higher understanding. The answer is that it can contribute a good deal. By concentrating on an analytical, deterministic method it has found ways to do some things better than any other single system in the history of humanity. Faced with a bleeding or torn limb, or with some other mechanical malfunction, it is the best treatment around. But in other cases it confines itself to dealing with the symptoms of illness alone: the antihistamine prescribed for hay fever and the valium given for nerves both deal entirely with the surface of the problem.

In these cases the flower remedies provide a way in which a deeper solution can be sought. There is no problem in continuing to take the antihistamine, of course, because it will at least help stop you from sneezing – but a cure will only be found by uncovering the mental and emotional states that leave you open to attack in the first place. Once this is done the physical problem will more often than not clear up of its own accord.

What then of other forms of alternative or complementary medicine? Do they have a role to play as well? The answer can only be yes. The flower remedies discovered by Dr Bach are a complete system in themselves, but there is always more than one way to approach a solution. Just as the Bach flower remedies and conventional medicine can complement each other, so aromatherapy, herbalism, massage, reflexology, acupuncture and so on can bring new flavours to the treatment that can in certain circumstances aid the individual's progress towards health.

The only word of warning is that in following the holistic, inclusive path suggested here, you should not forget all distinctions between the different systems. Just as your local pharmacist would be foolish to try to dispense aspirin and penicillin according to your character type and the mood you are in, so attempts to select flower remedies by using tarot cards, pendulums or laying on hands are at best misguided. Remedies chosen this way will not do any harm, since none of the remedies is poisonous, but if the right ones are selected this will be a matter of luck rather than insight. It cannot be stressed enough that the flower remedies are only really successful when they are selected for individuals on the basis of a sensitive appraisal of each individual's character and emotional state.

Dr Bach's flower remedies have been with us for most of the twentieth century and in that time their use has spread to all corners of the globe. As more and more people turn against the excesses of our industrial past and look for a more balanced way of life, their progress can only continue. This would have been a great source of satisfaction to the doctor who gave up his Harley Street practice in order to teach his patients how to heal themselves.

CHAPTER 15

Finding Help and Advice

Most people in the West are not used to taking responsibility for their own health. We prefer to leave the matter to professionals, carting ourselves off to the doctor's surgery when something goes wrong in much the same way that we would take a faulty car to the garage. As we have seen, this is fine for injuries and mechanical malfunctions – but in other respects human beings are more than machines and need to be treated as such. Unfortunately, and precisely because we are not used to taking care of ourselves, a system of self-healing such as the flower remedies can seem rather difficult at first.

As this book should have shown, there is really nothing in the flower remedy system to justify this lack of confidence. Flower remedies are for everyone, and with a little thought and a willingness to be objective about yourself you too can soon be in a position to take charge of your own well-being. But for those who would like extra help with the first steps, for those who are faced with particularly stubborn problems, or for those who would simply like to learn more about the remedies and their uses, there are a number of things you can do.

The first and perhaps easiest way to learn more is to read more. There are a number of books in print that deal with the remedies and particular aspects of their history and use. You would be especially well advised to read Dr Bach's own descriptions of the remedy plants and the character types associated with them. These can be found in *The Twelve Healers and Other Remedies*. This booklet was first published in the 1930s when Dr Bach had only discovered the first twelve remedies in his system. When it was enlarged to include the full thirty-eight the original title of the book was retained, as by then it had already become well known in the healing world. For full details of this and other recommended titles, see the appendix on pages 255–6.

Apart from books, the best source of information on this subject is the Dr Edward

Bach Centre in Oxfordshire, England. This is housed in the cottage where Dr Bach spent the final years of his life, and the mother tinctures are still produced here following his original instructions. The custodians of the Bach Centre provide videos, cassettes and books as well as offering free advice to those who need help with the remedies. Through the Dr Edward Bach Foundation they also run a professional training scheme designed to equip people who want to set up their own consultation service, or who want to include the use of the remedies in an existing therapeutic practice.

Finally, if you want to obtain the remedies ready-made but are having trouble finding a local stockist, there are a couple of places that can help. The Bach Centre can tell you where to obtain the remedies locally, whether you live in Britain or abroad. And if you would sooner obtain them by post, then Nelsons Homoeopathic Pharmacy runs a mail-order service within the UK. The addresses of the Pharmacy and of the Bach Centre can be found on page 256.

ATTENDING A CONSULTATION

The register of approved local practitioners held by the Bach Centre is a useful first step to finding someone near you who can help you to select the remedies you need. People do not always find it easy to be honest with themselves, especially in emotional matters, and a friendly but objective eye can be especially useful for beginners. A good counsellor will be able to advise you on your character type and suggest underlying causes for the problems that you have. Even if you are fairly experienced at using the remedies, consulting a trained practitioner can still be a great way to gain new insights into yourself and your relationship with the flower remedies.

Consultations are as individual as the people who run them, but even so there are some things that you will find at nearly all the consultations you attend. First, an effort will be made to put you at your ease so that you will be more likely to respond to the counsellor's questions. You will be asked why you have come, and if there is any specific problem that you need help with. As you answer, the counsellor may make notes on a pad. Sometimes these will be directly related to the answers you give, but at other times they might be general observations about your behaviour and attitude and, of course, any remedies that she feels might be able to help you. You might be asked further questions about your reactions to particular events, or how you feel when such-and-such a thing occurs. Sometimes these questions can seem irrelevant, but they are designed to help the counsellor decide which of two or more possible remedies is the correct one to select. Sometimes the counsellor may not need to ask questions at all – don't worry about this, as it simply means that you are providing enough information already.

The time it takes to complete a consultation varies tremendously, as no two individuals or their problems are alike. It may take only ten minutes to pinpoint the right remedies; but it is just as likely to be an hour or more before you are presented with the list of remedies that the counsellor thinks are right for you. At this stage you may want to discuss with her the different remedies selected and the reasons for each decision made.

The counsellor will either make up a treatment bottle for you on the spot or will tell you how to obtain the remedies and make up your own. She will probably ask you to come back for a second consultation. This is because as the remedies begin to work other underlying factors may emerge which require a slight alteration to the mix of remedies. At other times the treatment may not appear to be working at all. In this case the counsellor will want to review the selection of remedies to see which ingredients in the treatment bottle need to be changed.

Most counsellors will of course make a charge for the consultation and for making up a treatment bottle, but the exact amount varies, so it is wise to ask about this at the outset.

Appendix

FURTHER READING

All the books listed here were consulted during the writing of this book. Those marked with an *asterisk were especially useful, and are highly recommended to those who want to pursue the subject further.

Books by Dr Bach:

* Dr Edward Bach, *The Twelve Healers and Other Remedies* (C.W. Daniel Company, 3rd revised edition, Saffron Walden, 1936)

Dr Edward Bach, *Heal Thyself* (C.W. Daniel Company, Saffron Walden, 1931)

Judy Howard and John Ramsell (eds), *The Original Writings of Edward Bach* (C.W. Daniel Company, Saffron Walden, 1990)

Practical guides:

* Philip Chancellor, *Illustrated Handbook of the Bach Flower Remedies* (C.W. Daniel Company, Saffron Walden, 1971)

* Judy Howard, *The Bach Flower Remedies Step by Step* (C.W. Daniel Company, Saffron Walden, 1990)

* Judy Howard, *Bach Flower Remedies for Women* (C.W. Daniel Company, Saffron Walden, 1992)

* Judy Howard, *Growing up with Bach Flower Remedies* (C.W. Daniel Company, Saffron Walden, 1994)

* T.W. Hyne-Jones, *Dictionary of the Bach Flower Remedies* (C.W. Daniel Company, Saffron Walden, 1976)

John Ramsell, *Questions and Answers* (Bach Centre, 1986)

Mechthild Scheffer, *Bach Flower Therapy* (Thorsons, London, 1990)

Nora Weeks and Victor Bullen, *The Bach Flower Remedies: Illustrations and Preparations* (C.W. Daniel Company, Saffron Walden, 1964)

F.J. Wheeler, *The Bach Remedies Repertory* (C.W. Daniel Company, Saffron Walden, 1952)

On the history of Dr Bach and his discoveries:

Judy Howard, *The Story of Mount Vernon* (Bach Centre, 1987)

Nora Weeks, *The Medical Discoveries of Edward Bach, Physician* (C.W. Daniel Company, Saffron Walden, 1940)

Useful addresses:

For all general information, lists of suppliers, educational activities and publications, send a large stamped addressed envelope to:

The Dr Edward Bach Centre
Mount Vernon
Sotwell
Wallingford
Oxon OX10 0PZ

Ready-made remedies by mail order (UK only):

Nelsons Homoeopathic Pharmacy
73 Duke Street
London W1M 6BY